HORSE ANATOMY

A Coloring Atlas

2nd Edition

Robert A. Kainer, DVM, MS
Professor Emeritus of Anatomy
College of Veterinary Medicine and Biomedical Sciences
Colorado State University

Thomas O. McCracken, MS
Vice President for Product and Development
Visible Productions LLC, Fort Collins, Colorado;
formerly Associate Professor and Director,
Biomedical Illustration and Communications
College of Veterinary Medicine and Biomedical Sciences
Colorado State University

Alpine
PUBLICATIONS
Loveland, Colorado

Horse Anatomy, A Coloring Atlas
Second Edition

ISBN 1-57779-017-0 softcover; 1-57779-021-9 wire bound

Alpine books are available at special quantity discounts for bulk purchases to clubs, breeders, or for educational use. Special books or book excerpts can also be created to fit special needs.

For details, write or telephone Special Markets, Alpine Publications, P. O. Box 7027, Loveland, CO 80537.

3 4 5 6 7 8 9 0

Printed in the United States of America.

CONTENTS

Acknowledgments

The authors express their gratitude to Dave Carlson and Frank Forney for the design of the cover and to Sandra Mullins for its well-executed painting.

The critical review of the narrative and drawings by master anatomy instructors, Michael D. Smith and Dr. Tom Spurgeon, is greatly appreciated. Their thoughtful contributions are present throughout the atlas.

Special thanks are due to Sean McCracken for his patient labeling and preparation of the drawings.

Anne Ricciardi's careful organization of the manuscript is gratefully acknowledged.

Sharon Anderson's proof reading and suggestions enhanced the final manuscript.

Several modified illustrations in the atlas were redrawn with gracious consent from the following sources:

1. Amann, R.P.: Functional anatomy in the adult male in "Equine Reproduction", McKinnon, A. O. and Voss, J. L. (eds.), Philadelphia, Lea & Febiger, 1993. Figures 76-1,76-7, 76-12 and 76-13 drawn by John Daugherty.

2. DeLahunta, A. and Habel, R.E. : "Applied Veterinary Anatomy", Philadelphia, W.B. Saunders Company, 1986. Figure 6-1.

3. Dyce, K.M., Sack, W.O. and Wensing, C.J.G.: "Textbook of Veterinary Anatomy", Philadelphia, W.B. Saunders Company, 1987. Figure 8-36.

4. Kainer, R.A.: Functional anatomy of equine locomotor organs in "Adams' Lameness in Horses", 4th Ed., Stashak, T. (ed.), Philadelphia, Lea & Febiger, 1987. Figures 1-4, 1-5, 1-13, 1-37 and 1-48 drawn by John Daugherty.

5. Kainer, R.A.: Reproductive organs of the mare in "Equine Reproduction", McKinnon, A.O. and Voss, J.L. (eds.), Philadelphia, Lea & Febiger, 1993. Figures 1-5, 1-6 and 1-14 drawn by Brian Evans.

6. Kainer, R.A.: Clinical anatomy of the equine head, Veterinary Clinics of North America: Equine Practice, 9: 1-23, 1993. Figures 6 and 7 drawn by Brian Evans.

PREFACE

This atlas is intended for use by those truly interested in horses - from 4H club groups to first-year veterinary medical students. Equine science majors, serious horsemen, trainers, breeders and farriers will find this approach a pleasant and rewarding way to learn equine anatomy.

Why learn some equine anatomy? Your reasons will vary, depending on your particular involvement with horses. Basically, a knowledge of the functional anatomy of the horse will give you the satisfaction of knowing your horse better, providing:

> Understanding of the structural basis for the horse's main function, **locomotion,**
> An appreciation of the horse's gaits as it carries or pulls us (or something else) along,
> A background for communication with other horse owners, trainers, farriers and veterinarians, especially with regard to the function or malfunction of the organs of locomotion, digestion, respiration and reproduction,
> And the satisfaction of knowing your horse better.

Horses and their close relatives, donkeys and zebras, are in the mammalian order of odd-toed, hoofed animals (Perissodactyla) as are its distant relatives, rhinoceroses and tapirs. The horse, Equus caballus, is an **equid**, a member of the horse family, Equidae. The adjective, equine, is frequently used improperly as a noun.

Characteristics of equids include:
1. Highly specialized limbs, each with one digit (the third) and with the main muscle mass of the limb situated close to the body's trunk,
2. Large paranasal sinuses within the skull,
3. Guttural pouches, large outpocketings of the auditory tubes that extend from the nasopharynx to the middle ears,
4. High-crowned permanent teeth which grow for a long time, a feature used to determine the age of horses,
5. A simple stomach followed by a long small intestine and a large, complicated large intestine where fermentation of feed occurs,
6. Well-developed skin glands,
7. Large heart and lungs,
8. A uterus with short horns and a relatively large body, a prominent depression in each ovary where the egg cells are released,
9. A large, vascular penis and a complete set of male accessory sex glands.

THE AUTHORS

Robert A. Kainer, DVM, MS
Professor Emeritus of Anatomy
College of Veterinary Medicine and Biomedical Sciences.
Colorado State University, Fort Collins, Colorado

After receiving his DVM degree from Colorado A & M College (now CSU) in 1949, Dr, Kainer spent a summer at the University of Idaho, then four years at Washington State University where he taught anatomy and pursued graduate study in anatomy and pathology. He earned a Master of Science degree in veterinary medicine from Washington State and subsequently taught for two years in the Department of Veterinary Pathology at Oklahoma State University. He entered private veterinary practice in Idaho Springs, Colorado in 1955. But the call to teach was persistent, and he served as a high school science teacher while in practice. In 1961, he returned to Colorado State University as a member of the anatomy faculty. Among the honors he received during 27 years at CSU are the Top Prof Award, the Oliver Pennock Award for teaching and scholarship, the Norden Award for distinguished teaching in veterinary medicine, Outstanding Educator of America, 1973, and the Colorado Veterinary Medical Association 1986 Faculty of the Year Award. Dr. Kainer has contributed his expertise to research papers and textbooks, resulting in over 60 publications. His recent research interests have centered on the biology and heat treatment of certain eye and skin tumors in cattle and horses.

Thomas O. McCracken, MS
Vice President for Product and Development
Visible Productions LLC
Fort Collins, Colorado

Mr. McCracken graduated from the University of Michigan in 1968 with a bachelor's degree in biology. He attended graduate school at the same institution, receiving master's degrees in medical illustration, anatomy and physiology. In 1975, Mr. McCracken went to Saudi Arabia where he served for two years as chief medical illustrator for the King Faisal Specialist Hospital at Riyadh. Upon returning from Arabia, he was appointed Director of Biomedical Media in the College of Veterinary Medicine and Biomedical Sciences at Colorado State University. From 1978 to 1985, he illustrated five veterinary medical textbooks and over 75 scientific papers. In 1985, he was appointed to the faculty of the Department of Anatomy and Neurobiology, and in 1990, he became director of the sixth accredited medical illustration program in the United States. Mr. McCracken resigned from CSU in 1994 to enter private enterprise, eventually assuming the vice presidency of Visible Productions. Over the years, Mr. McCracken has won numerous awards of excellence from the Association of Medical Illustrators for his anatomical and surgical illustrations. In 1997, he was the recipient of the Frank Netter Award for special contributions to medical education.

HOW TO USE THIS COLORING ATLAS

Using this atlas, you will explore the horse's body by coloring drawings of its various organs and reading the short descriptions accompanying the drawings. Coloring illustrations in this manner is an enjoyable and effective learning experience. In keeping with the current trend, most Latin anatomic names have been changed to English.

Drawings of **organs** making up the **systems** of the horse's body are presented in plates. Pages opposite the plates contain labels for coloring the drawings. Essential anatomic and physiologic concepts are explained and some common diseases are presented. Important terms are underlined in the text.

The atlas may be used alone, or it may be used to assist in dissections. Many of the plates are drawn from prosected specimens. For the most part, each plate is self-contained, so the plates do not have to be studied in sequence. You may select those you wish to color first or to review later.

Before beginning, read the following important directions:
1. Look over the entire plate on the right page, and then read labeling instructions on the left page. Structures to be colored are printed in **boldface type** preceded by numbers or letters that correspond with numbers or letters indicating structures on the drawings on the plate.
2. Underline the words in **boldface type** on the left page in different colors, and use the same colors on the indicated structures, arrows or dashed lines on the drawings. Also color in the words written in open-faced letters on the drawings.
3. The choice of colors is yours. Colored pencils or felt-tipped pens are recommended. Very dark colors obscure detail, so use lighter shades of these colors and test the colors before using them.

Suggested coloring utensils include Crayola ® Washable Markers, Pentel ® Color Pens, colored artist pencils, or other similar media.

SURFACE OF THE BODY

EXTERNAL REGIONS OF THE HORSE'S BODY

Plate 1

1. Poll
2. Forehead
3. Face
4. Nostril
5. Lips
6. Jaw
7. Throatlatch
8. Crest
9. Neck
10. Jugular groove
11. Withers
12. Shoulder
13. Point of shoulder

   (middle of the shoulder joint)

14. Chest
15. Arm
16. Elbow
17. Forearm
18. Carpus or knee
19. Metacarpus or forecannon
20. Fetlock or ankle
21. Pastern
22. Coronet

   (joins skin of 21 & 23)

23. Hoof
24. Thorax or barrel
25. Girth
26. Abdomen or belly

27. Flank
28. Back
29. Loin
30. Croup
31. Point of hip

   (coxal tuber)

32. Tailhead
33. Buttock
34. Thigh or quarter
35. Stifle
36. Leg or gaskin
37. Tarsus or hock
38. Metatarsus or hindcannon

Color regions of the digit (21,22,23) on the other limbs (Not legs!).
The modern horse walks on its third digit (your middle finger).
Note that the **manus** (Latin for hand) extends from the carpus (included) to the ground.
The **pes** (Latin for foot) extends from the tarsus (included) to the ground.

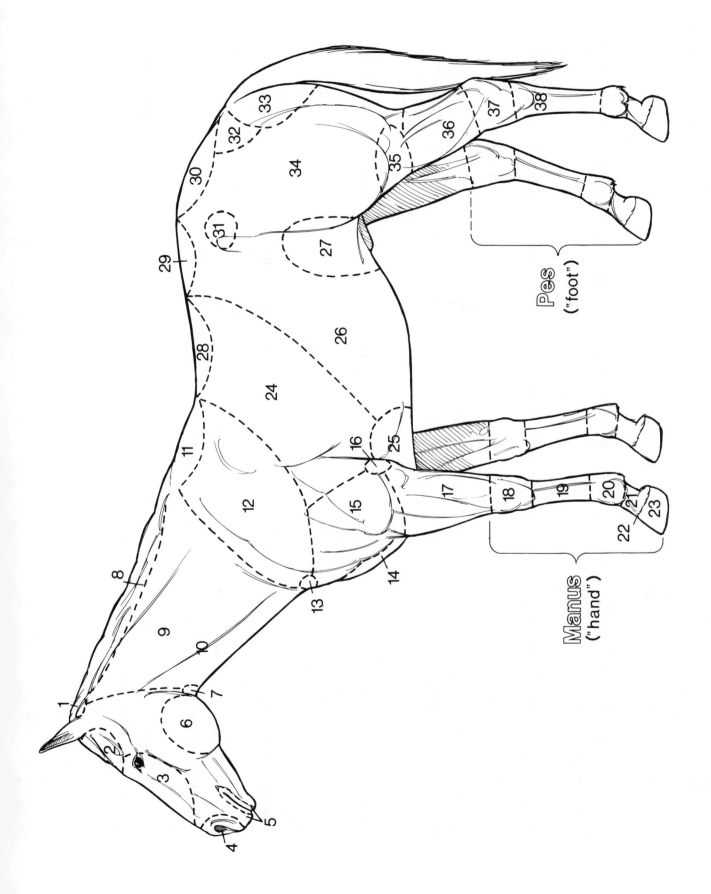

Manus ("hand")

Pes ("foot")

Plate 1

This is a view of the near side (left side) of a horse. The right side is the off side.

Directional terms describe the location of parts of the body, relate functional changes in position, and define the extent of lesions (diseased regions).

Dorsal (A to B) and **ventral** (C to D) are opposite terms indicating relative locations of parts toward the back (dorsum) or the belly (venter).

Above the carpus or knee and above the hock (dotted lines) and from the belly to the back, a structure located closer to the cranium (skull case) is **cranial** to another structure, and a structure located toward the tail (cauda) is **caudal** to an-other.

On the head, notice the dashed line from A to E. Here, the term, **rostral**, is used to show the location of a structure closer to the nose (rostrum). Caudal remains the same.

Proximal indicates a location toward the attached end of a limb.
Distal indicates a location toward the free end of a limb, that is, further from the body.

Distal to and including the carpus, **dorsal** replaces cranial and **palmar** replaces caudal.
Distal to and including the hock, **dorsal** replaces cranial, but **plantar** replaces caudal.

On a frontal view of the distal end of a horse's limb, the axis is shown by a dashed line. An **axial** structure is located to-ward the axis; an **abaxial** structure, away from it.

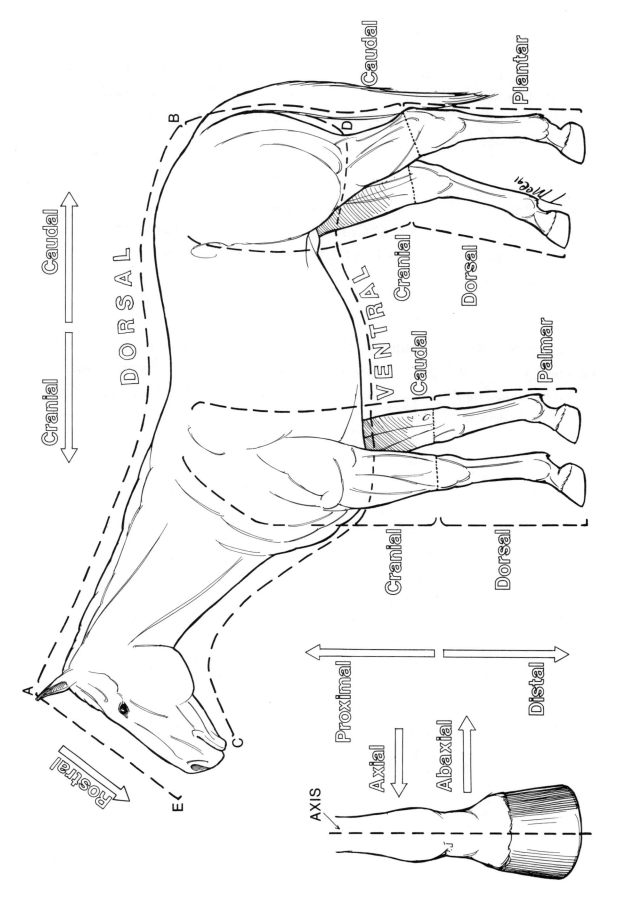

Plate 2

Figure 1. The **median plane** (L., medianus = in the middle), indicated by the dashed lines between the m's, divides the horse's body into right and left halves. A **sagittal plane** (L., sagitta = arrow), indicated by the dashed line from s to s, is any plane parallel to the median plane.

Figure 2. The **median plane** is indicated by the dashed line. **Medial and lateral** (L., latus = side) are directional terms relative to the median plane. Medial structures are located closer to the median plane. Lateral structures lie away from the median plane, that is, toward the side.

Figure 3. A **transverse plane,** indicated by the dashed lines between the t's, passes through the head, trunk or limb perpendicular to the part's long axis. A **dorsal plane** (frontal plane), indicated by the dashed line from d to d, passes through a body part parallel to its dorsal surface.

Plate 3

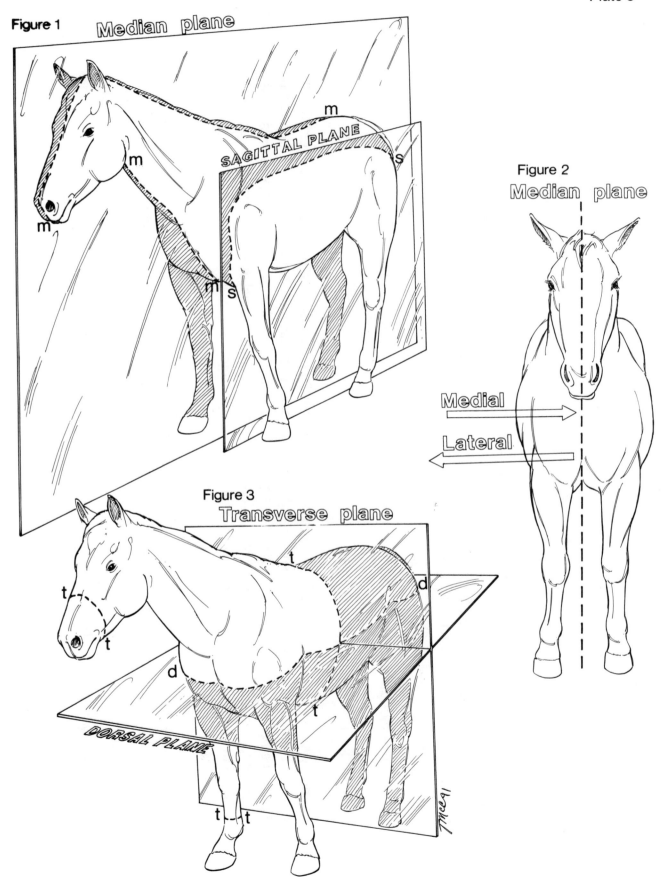

Figure 1

Median plane

SAGITTAL PLANE

m
m
m
m s
s

Figure 2

Median plane

Medial

Lateral

Figure 3

Transverse plane

t
t
t
d
d
t
t
t

DORSAL PLANE

Plate 4

GROSS FEATURES OF EQUINE SKIN

This is a drawing of a Clydesdale gelding (castrated male).

Use dark lines for the coarse hairs of the **forelock, mane** and **tail. Tactile** (feeling) **hairs** protrude from the skin around the eyelids, nostrils and lips.

Outline the white **blaze** in color and lightly color most of the horse's skin this shade.
A bald face is wider than a blaze.
A star is a white area in the middle of the forehead.
A stripe is a long, narrow white area.
A snip is a white stripe between the nostrils.

Leave the **stockings** and **feathers** white, coloring the words. Most horses do not have so much feathering.

The **prepuce** is the sheath of the penis.

The horny **chestnuts or night-eyes** are proximal to the carpus (here also termed carpal pads) and distal to the hock (here also termed tarsal pads). Their shape and patterning is used to help identify horses, mainly Thoroughbreds. Parting the hairs on the palmar (on the forelimb) or plantar (on the hindlimb) surface of a fetlock reveals another horny outgrowth of the epidermis (outer layer of the skin), an **ergot.** Chestnuts are believed to be vestiges (evolutinary remnants) of the carpal and tarsal pads of carnivores (dogs, bears). Ergots are considered vestiges of metacarpal and metatarsal pads.

Hooves are also epidermal structures (similar to your fingernails).
Color the **hoof of the forefoot** black, indicating pigment, and the **hooves of the hindfeet** yellow, indicating lack of pigment.

The hoof below the view of the ergot is shod, that is, a shoe is nailed to it.

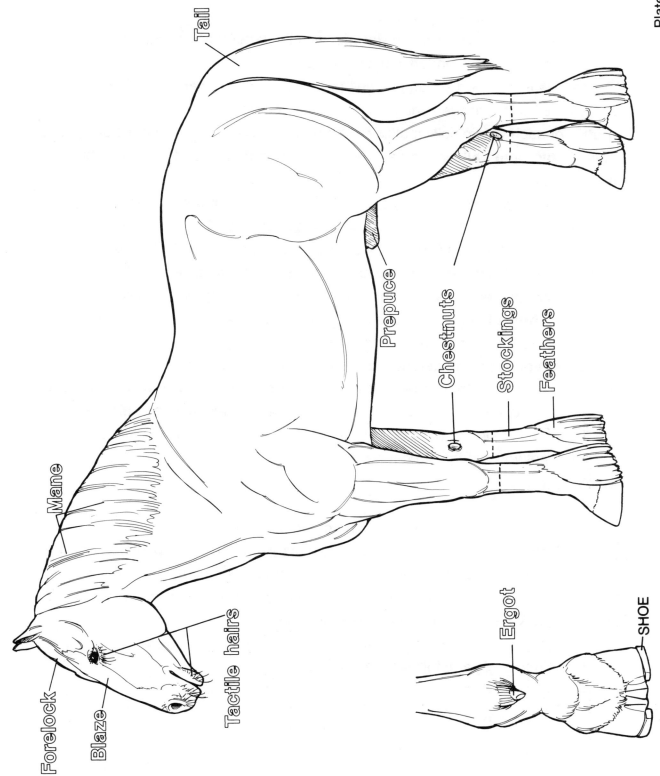

Tail

Prepuce

Chestnuts

Stockings

Feathers

Mane

Forelock

Blaze

Tactile hairs

Ergot

SHOE

Plate 4

Figure 1. Haired skin from the neck.

Skin consists of **epidermis and dermis,** with the latter blending into the **subcutis** which attaches skin to underlying structures.

Epidermis is <u>stratified</u> <u>squamous</u> <u>epithelium</u>, a highly cellular tissue with flat, horny surface cells. This tissue continues into a **hair follicle** and down to the **hair bulb matrix** of each where cells multiply to form the hair. Make dots with a black pencil to indicate **pigment cells** in the deep layers of the epidermis and in the hair bulb matrix.

Dermis is <u>dense</u> <u>fibrous</u> (<u>collagenous</u>) <u>tissue</u>, and the deeper **subcutis** is <u>loose connective</u> <u>tissue</u> containing depots of <u>fat</u> (<u>adipose</u> <u>tissue</u>).

Two types of cutaneous (skin) glands empty into hair follicles. Cells produced by **sebaceous (oil) glands** break up to form the oily secretion, <u>sebum</u>. **Apocrine tubular glands** secrete <u>sweat</u> and are commonly called <u>sweat</u> <u>glands</u>.

Sensory nerves bring sensations of pressure, pain, heat and cold from nerve endings in the dermis just under the epidermis.

Motor nerves (from the autonomic nervous system) cause apocrine tubular glands to secrete and smooth muscle cells of the **hair erector muscles** to contract. Contractions of these muscles elevate hairs and squeeze on sebaceous glands.

On the left hand side of the block of skin notice that **blood vessels** branch and join to form 3 networks in the subcutis and skin. Locate the blood supply to the hair bulbs.

Figure 2. Nonhaired skin from the lining of the prepuce.

In this block of skin from the lining of the <u>prepuce</u> (sheath of the penis) notice the thick epidermis with pegs projecting into the dermis. Large quantities of sebum termed **smegma** are produced by well-developed **sebaceous glands. Apocrine tubular glands** also empty into the glandular pores.

(Text continued on page following drawing.)

Plate 5

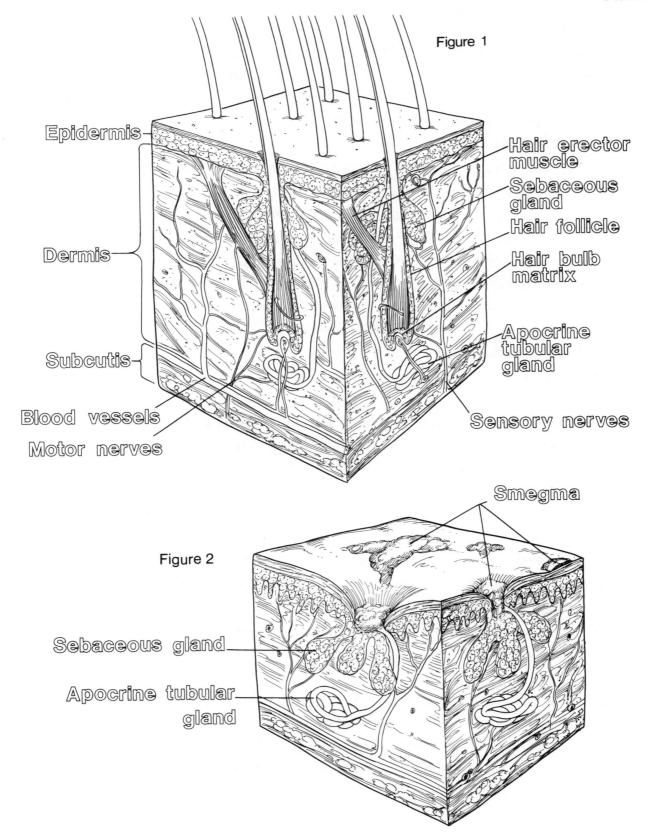

Figure 1

Epidermis

Dermis

Subcutis

Blood vessels

Motor nerves

Hair erector muscle

Sebaceous gland

Hair follicle

Hair bulb matrix

Apocrine tubular gland

Sensory nerves

Smegma

Figure 2

Sebaceous gland

Apocrine tubular gland

SIGNIFICANT INFORMATION ON THE HORSE'S SKIN

The skin is the body's largest organ. It interfaces with the environment, serving as a barrier to living, chemical and physical agents and providing sensory information. Other functions are flexible support, control of water loss, immunologic responses, regulation of blood pressure and control of body temperature. Changes in blood flow, erection of hairs and sweating influence body temperature.

Profuse sweating by horses is called lathering. Sweating is important in cooling the animal, and horses which sweat heavily should receive a supplemental salt mixture to replace salts lost in sweating. A hot, sweaty horse should be walked until it cools down. Secretion of sweat by apocrine tubular glands is stimulated by motor nerves and by the hormone, epinephrine, (adrenalin) secreted into the blood by the adrenal glands. A "nervous" horse can begin to sweat. Secretions by skin glands cleanse hair follicles and discourage the growth of harmful organisms.

"Sweating" is a procedure in which a tightly fitting plastic wrap is covered over a mild stimulant on a part of a horse's body (usually the neck), causing the covered area to sweat profusely. This dehydrates the region and tightens its profile for display in the show ring for a short time after removal of the plastic wrap. Later, when the horse drinks, fluid is restored to the tissues. This procedure is also used to reduce swelling of chronically inflamed parts of limbs.

Horses shed hair mostly in the spring, beginning on the belly and sides and continuing up onto the back. The hair cycle includes an actively growing stage (anagen) followed by a stage (catagen) during which the hair matrix sort of shrinks (atrophies) and peels away from its blood supply. A longer quiescent period (telogen) then occurs in which the hair (club hair) separates from the hair matrix but remains in the follicle. The matrix later becomes active and begins to grow a new hair that pushes out the old club hair (shedding).

Masses of smegma (sometimes called "beans") frequently need to be cleaned from the male horse's prepuce with mild soap and water.
The mare's udder consists of mammary glands, highly developed and modified apocrine tubular glands. Sebaceous gland secretions form a dark layer on the skin between the halves of the udder. This layer may be scraped off.

ORGANS OF LOCOMOTION

Plate 6

SKELETON OF THE HORSE

AXIAL SKELETON

1. Skull
2. Mandible
3. Hyoid bone

4. Vertebral column
5. Ribs

6. Costal cartilages
7. Sternum

APPENDICULAR SKELETON

FORELIMB

8. Scapular cartilage
9. Scapula
10. Humerus
11. Radius
12. Ulna
13. Carpal bones - 7 or 8

14. Metacarpal bones - 3
    (3rd Mc = cannon bone)
15. Proximal sesamoid bones - 2
16. Proximal phalanx
    (First phalanx or P1)
    (Plural = phalanges)

17. Middle phalanx
    (Second phalanx or P2)
18. Distal sesamoid bone
    (Navicular bone)
19. Distal phalanx
    (Third phalanx or P3)
    (Coffin bone or pedal bone)

20. Ilium ⎤
21. Pubis ⎬ Fused to form the hip bone
22. Ischium ⎦ (os coxae)

23. Femur

HINDLIMB

24. Patella
25. Tibia
26. Fibula
27. Tarsal bones - 6
28. Metatarsal bones - 3

Digital bones of the hindlimb are named the same as those of the forelimb, nos. 16 - 19.

There are 205 bones in the horse's skeleton. Thirty-four, including 3 auditory (hearing) ossicles in each temporal bone, are in the skull. The twenty bones in each forelimb and the twenty in each hindlimb are of great importance in health and disease, since they form the basis for locomotion.

Plate 6

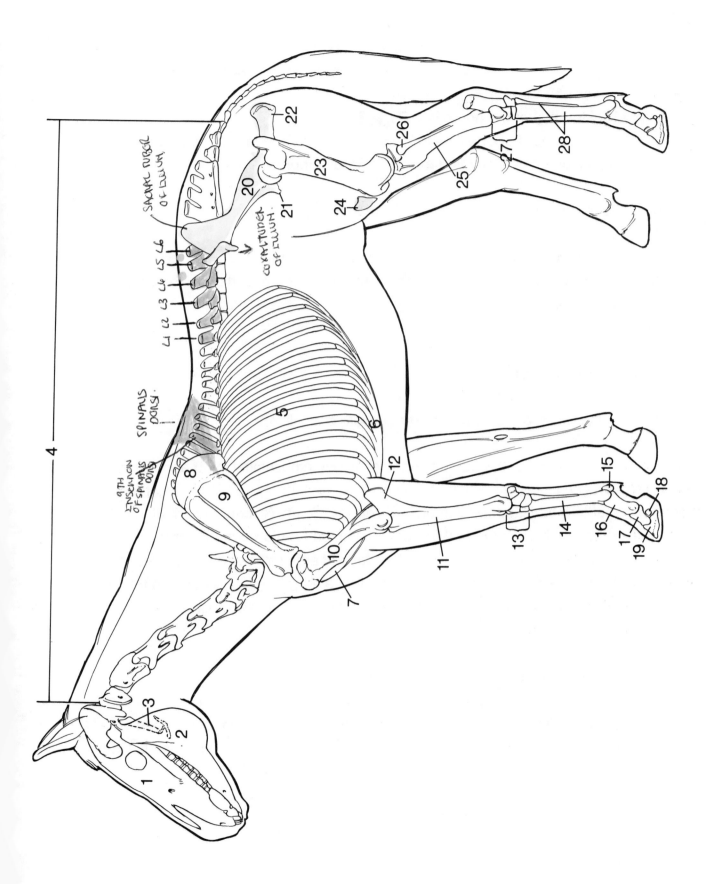

SACRAL TUBER OF ILIUM

SPINALIS DORSI.

9TH INSERTION OF SPINALIS DORSI

COXAL TUBER OF ILIUM

L1 L2 L3 L4 L5 L6

4

22

23

20

21

24

26

25

27

28

8

9

10

7

5

6

12

11

13

14

15

16

17

19

18

1

2

3

Figure 1. Regions of the vertebral (spinal) column.

Identify the regions and the number of vertebrae in each region:

7 cervical, 18 thoracic, 6 lumbar, 5 sacral (fused to form the sacrum), **and 15-21 caudal (coccygeal) vertebrae.**

The <u>vertebral</u> <u>formula</u> of the horse is $C_7T_{18}L_6S_5Ca_{15\text{-}21}$

There may be one more or one less thoracic vertebra or one less lumbar vertebra. The latter condition has been noted mainly in Arabian horses.

Figure 2. Vertebrae are irregular bones of various shapes.

Identify and color the following parts:

1. **Transverse processes (Wings** on the atlas and sacrum)
2. **Vertebral foramen** (Combined foramina form the vertebral canal which contains the spinal cord and its coverings.)
3. **Body**
4. **Arch**
5. **Spinous process(es)**
6. **Articular processes (Dens** of the axis)
7. **Articular surfaces of sacrum (Articulate** with each ilium)

Except for articulations of the **atlas** with the skull (atlantooccipital joint) and with the **axis** (atlantoaxial joint - a pivot joint), the bodies of vertebrae are joined by <u>intervertebral</u> <u>discs</u> of fibrocartilage. Movements of vertebral joints (except the atlantoaxial joint) are dorsal, ventral and lateral flexion and limited rotation. Spinal nerves emerge through foramina formed between arches of adjacent vertebrae or through lateral vertebral foramina in arches. On each side, a <u>vertebral</u> <u>artery</u> courses through foramina in the transverse processes of cervical vertebrae one through six on its way to supply the brain.

Malformation of certain cervical vertebrae is one of the most common causes of the <u>wobbler</u> <u>syndrome</u>. It is most prevalent in Thoroughbred and Quarter Horse males, but it can occur in all breeds and both sexes. Local constriction of the vertebral canal exerts pressure on the spinal cord, interfering with nerve impulses to limb muscles.

Plate 7

Figure 1

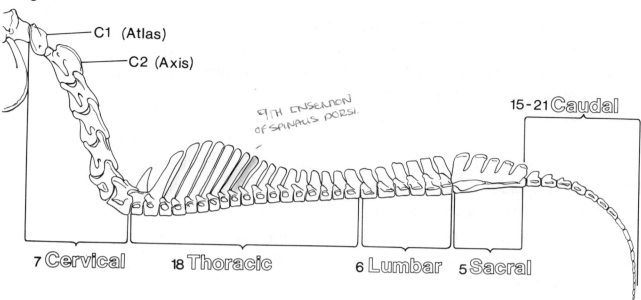

C1 (Atlas)

C2 (Axis)

9TH INSERTION
OF SPINALIS DORSI.

15-21 Caudal

7 Cervical

18 Thoracic

6 Lumbar

5 Sacral

Figure 2

Atlas

Axis

Thoracic
vertebra

Sacrum

Lumbar vertebra

The horse has 18 (occasionally 19) pairs of **ribs. Costal cartilages** of the first 8 pairs of true ribs articulate with the **sternum;** the rest are false (asternal) ribs. Final ribs which lack costal cartilage attachment to adjacent cartilages are floating ribs. Fused costal cartilages form the costal arch. (L., costa = rib).

The **head** of each rib articulates with the bodies of adjacent thoracic vertebrae, the first rib articulating with the 7th cervical and 1st thoracic vertebrae. The **tubercle** on most ribs articulates with the transverse process on the caudal vertebra of the two with which the head articulates. On the caudal ribs in the series, the tubercle approaches the head and eventually fuses with it.

Figure 1. Craniocaudal view of first ribs, first thoracic vertebra and sternum.

1. Left 1st rib	**4. Neck**
2. Transverse process of T1	**5. Head**
3. Tubercle	**6. Sternum**

Figure 2. Medial view of right 7th rib. Notice the costochondral and chondrosternal junctions (Greek, chondros = cartilage).

3. Tubercle	**6. Sternum**
4. Neck	**7. Right 7th costal cartilage**
5. Head	

The **sternum** consists of 7 **sternebrae** which never become completely bony. The cranial segment, the **manubrium,** presents a cartilage as does the caudal segment, the **xiphoid process,** from which the **xiphoid cartilage** projects.

Figure 3. Dorsal view of the horse's sternum.

8. First 8 ribs	**12. Sternebrae 2 to 6**
9. Costal cartilages	**13. Xiphoid process**
10. Cartliage of the manubrium	**14. Xiphoid cartilage**
11. Manubrium	

Plate 8

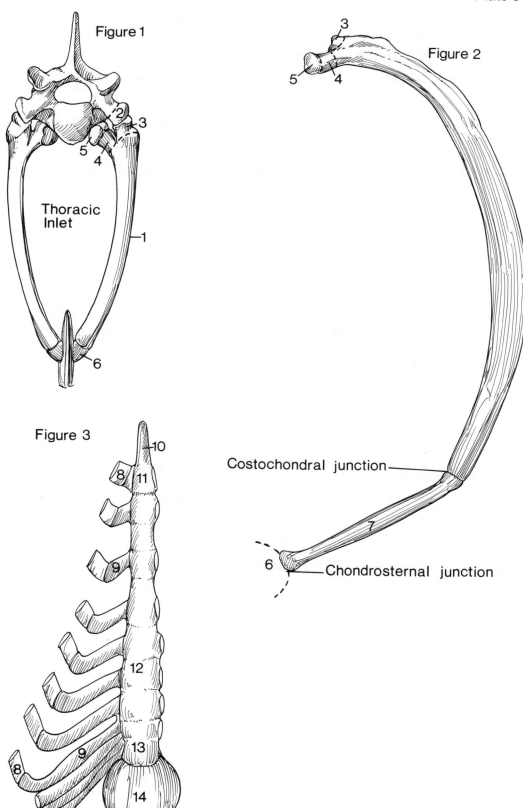

Figure 1

Thoracic
Inlet

Figure 2

Figure 3

Costochondral junction

Chondrosternal junction

Longitudinal section of a mature equine humerus.

1. **Diaphysis (shaft)** - Arrow shows extent.

2. **Epiphysis (end)** - Arrows indicate an epiphysis at the proximal end and one at the distal end of the bone.

3. **Epiphyseal line** - Each epiphyseal line is the region of the final replacement of cartilage by bone.

4. **Periosteum** - This is the vessel-rich, bone-producing membrane covering the bone (dashed line) except over the ends covered by articular cartilage.

5. **Articular cartilage** - Smooth, hyaline (glassy) cartilage covers the end of a bone where it meets another bone in a joint.

6. **Cancellous (spongy) bone** - Bony trabeculae (little beams) give support against stresses placed on the bone. Red marrow (source of most blood cells) occupies spaces among the trabeculae.

7. **Compact bone** - This tissue is formed by densely-packed, cylindrical osteons of cells and bone containing channels for blood vessels.

8. **Marrow cavity** - Fatty yellow marrow replaces red marrow in the marrow cavity.

9. **Endosteum** - Bone is laid down by this membrane lining the marrow cavity.

10. **Nutrient artery** - Blood for the bone is supplied by vessels in the periosteum and by the nutrient artery carrying blood to the endosteum.

Most bones develop in a mass of cartilage; a few develop in a membrane of collagenous connective tissue. Bones may be classified by their shape: long, short, flat or irregular. The humerus is a long bone that developed in a cartilaginous model.

Plate 9

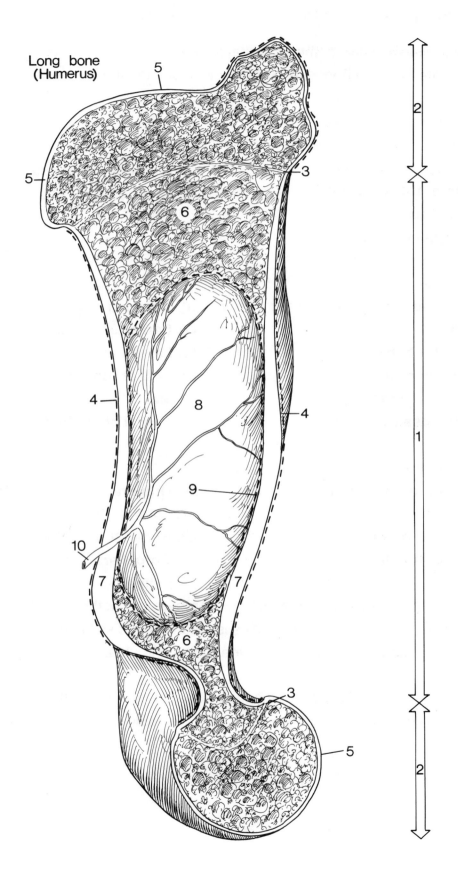

Long bone
(Humerus)

Lateral and medial views of the **scapula, humerus** and fused **ulna** and **radius** are
seen on Plate 10. The bones are slightly disarticulated to show joint surfaces.

On the scapula -
1. **Scapular cartilage**
2. **Supraspinous fossa**
3. **Spine of the scapula**
4. **Infraspinous fossa**
5. **Supraglenoid tubercle**

6. **Serrated face**
7. **Subscapular fossa**
8. **Coracoid process**
9. **Glenoid cavity**

On the humerus -
10. **Greater tubercle**
11. **Head**
12. **Deltoid tuberosity**
13. **Musculospiral groove**
14. **Olecranon fossa**
15. **Radial fossa**

16. **Trochlea** ⎫ of
17. **Capitulum** ⎬ condyle
18. **Lateral epicondyle**
19. **Lesser tubercle**
20. **Major teres tuberosity**
21. **Medial epicondyle**

On the ulna and radius -
22. **Olecranon tuberosity**
23. **Anconeal process**
24. **Trochlear notch**
25. **Shaft of the ulna**

26. **Humeral articular surface**
27. **Lateral styloid process**
28. **Radial tuberosity**
29. **Carpal articular surface of the radius**

The olecranon tuberosity and the anconeal process are both part of the **olecranon**.
The lateral styloid process on the radius is actually the distal end of the ulna.
An **interosseous space** lies between the radius and ulna.

Visualizing fractures on an x-ray film depends on knowledge of the bone involved.
The supraglenoid tubercle and the olecranon are common fracture sites in this
region.

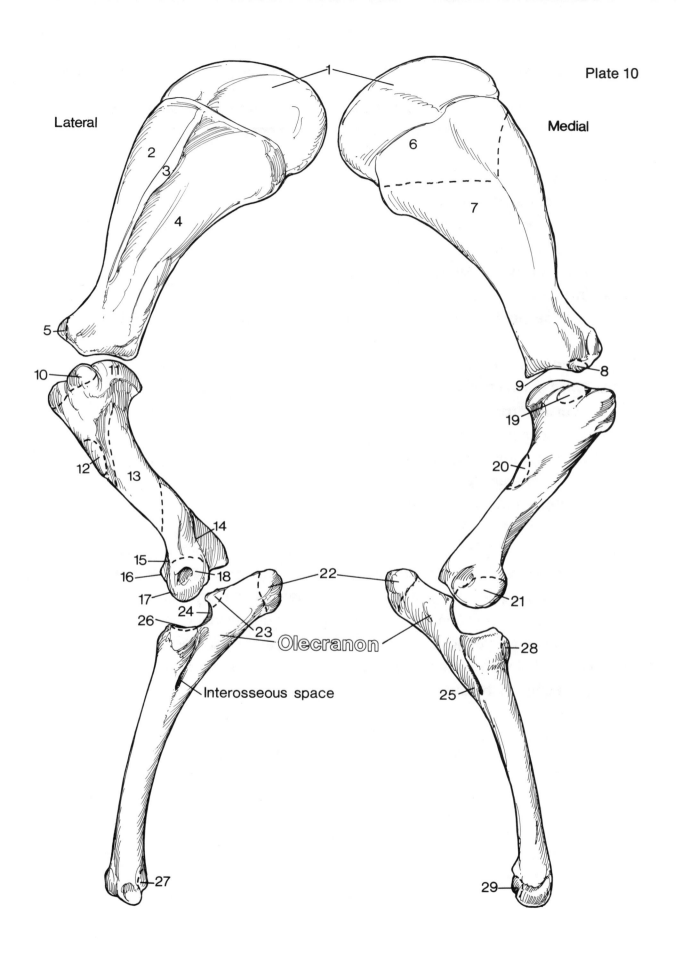

Plate 10

Lateral

Medial

1

2
3
4
5
6
7
8
9
10
11
12
13
14
15
16
17
18
19
20
21
22
23
24
25
26
27
28
29

Olecranon

Interosseous space

Dorsal, lateral and palmar views of the carpal bones are shown together with the articulating ends of the radius and metacarpal bones.

Proximal row:

RC Radial carpal bone

IC Intermediate carpal bone

UC Ulnar carpal bone

AC Accessory carpal bone

Distal row:

IC First carpal bone (Embedded in the medial collateral ligament of the carpus. It may be absent.)

2C Second carpal bone

3C Third carpal bone

4C Fourth carpal bone

Metacarpal bones:

2Mc Second metacarpal bone

3Mc Third metacarpal bone

4Mc Fourth metacarpal bone

Awareness of the details of the structure and relationships of carpal bones is essential to understanding the function of the horse's carpus (knee) and the causes and consequences of lameness due to defects or injury. For example, "calf knee" (palmar deviation of the carpus) is a conformational weakness. In this deformity and in young racehorses in general, carpal chip fractures commonly occur within the joints of the carpus in the radial, intermediate and third carpal bones and in the distal end of the radius.

Plate 11

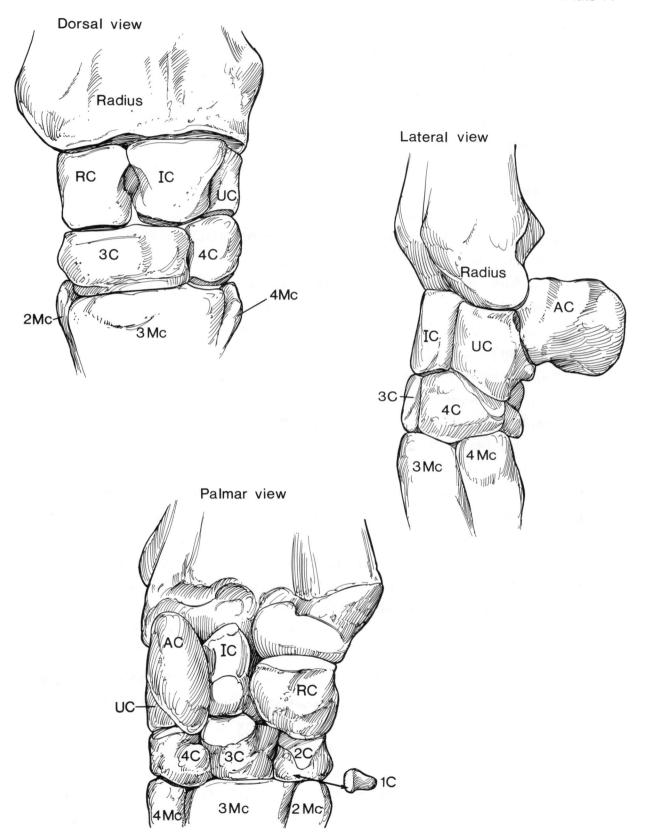

Dorsal view

Radius

RC   IC
           UC
  3C   4C
                4Mc
2Mc
      3Mc

Lateral view

Radius
                    AC
  IC   UC
3C
     4C
3Mc   4Mc

Palmar view

    AC   IC
              RC
UC
  4C   3C   2C
                  1C
4Mc   3Mc   2Mc

In the dorsal and palmar views of the right metacarpal and digital bones, the bones are disarticulated so that the articular surfaces may be seen.

2 Mc   Second (medial small) metacarpal bone (splint bone)

3 Mc   Third (large) metacarpal bone (cannon bone)

    1. Metacarpal tuberosity

    2. Ridge on distal articular surface

4.Mc   Fourth (lateral small) metacarpal bone (splint bone)

PSm   Medial proximal sesamoid bone

PSl   Lateral proximal sesamoid bone

PP   Proximal phalanx (first phalanx, P1, long pastern bone)

    3. Extensor process

MP   Middle phalanx (second phalanx, P2, short pastern bone)

DS   Distal sesamoid bone (navicular bone)

    4. Articular surface   5. Flexor surface

DP   Distal phalanx (third phalanx, P3, coffin bone)

    6. Extensor process   9. Flexor surface

    7. Parietal surface   10. Semilunar line

    8. Solar foramen   11. Solar surface

C   Cartilages of the distal phalanx

Alignment of bones is important in evaluating the conformation of the limb.

The proximal and distal sesamoid bones serve as pulleys that change the direction of the deep digital flexor tendon.

Notice the ridge on the distal articular surface of the third metacarpal bone and visualize how it might produce a "screwdriver fracture" of the proximal phalanx. Although the proximal sesamoid bones are deeply embedded in and supported by ligaments, they are subject to fractures. A variety of fractures can occur in the distal phalanx.

The navicular bone articulates with both the middle and distal phalanges. Progressive degeneration of the navicular bone results in navicular disease (See Plate 27).

As the horse ages, the cartilages of the distal phalanx tend to ossify (become bone), interfering with their flexibility and their ability to spread when the foot strikes the ground.

Sidebone is the complete ossification of the cartilages of the distal phalanx.

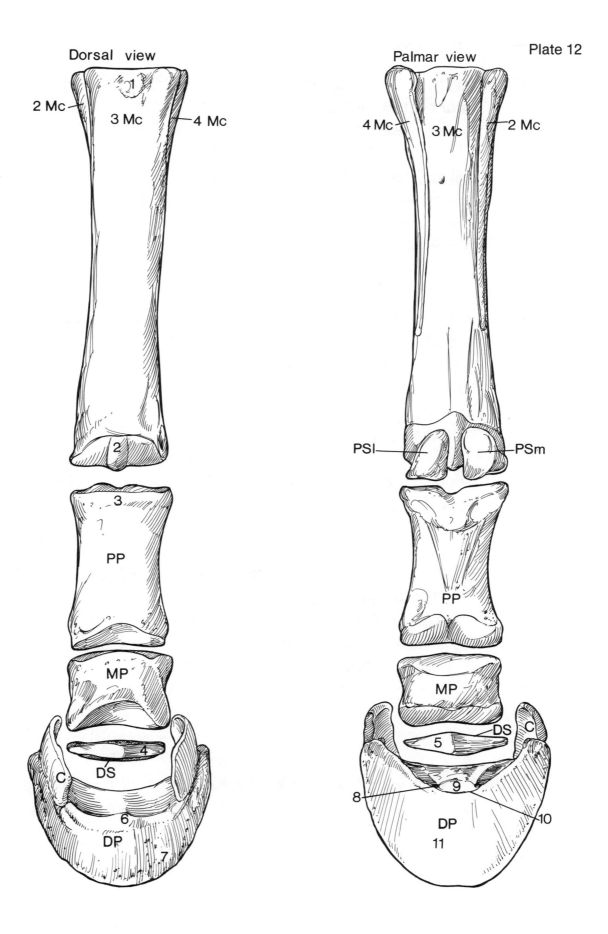

Dorsal view

2 Mc   3 Mc   4 Mc
1
2
3
PP
MP
4
DS
C
6
DP
7

Palmar view   Plate 12

4 Mc   3 Mc   2 Mc

PSl   PSm

PP

MP

DS   C
5
8   9   10
DP
11

Figure 1. <u>Fibrous</u> Joints - Immovable; fibrous tissue unites; ossify with age
>   **Suture** - Most joints of the skull
>   **Syndesmosis** - Between shafts of some long bones

Figure 2. <u>Cartilaginous</u> Joints - Limited movement; midline
>   **Symphysis** - Fibrocartilage; symphysis pelvis ossifies with age;
>   intervertebral discs do not normally ossify
>   **Growth plate (physis)** (arrows) - Hyaline cartilage grows and ossifies,
>   increasing a bone's length. It completely ossifies at maturity.

Figure 3. <u>Synovial</u> Joint - Drawn here in longitudinal section. Synovial (diarthrodial)
>   joints are movable. Parts of a typical synovial joint:
>   **Articular cartilages** - Hyaline cartilage
>   **Synovial membrane** - Produces lubricating <u>synovial</u> <u>fluid</u> ("<u>joint</u> <u>oil</u>")
>   **Fibrous joint capsule**
>   **Collateral ligaments** - Extra-articular
>
>   <u>Intra-articular</u> <u>ligaments</u> in the femorotibial joint are <u>not</u> <u>within</u> <u>the</u>
>   <u>synovial</u> <u>cavity</u>. In this joint <u>menisci</u> <u>of</u> <u>fibrocartilage</u> are placed between
>   the articulating bones.
>
>   Synovial joints are classified also on the basis of the <u>type</u> <u>of</u> <u>motion</u>.
>   Examples are given:
>   <u>Hinge</u> <u>joint</u> (ginglymus) - <u>Flexion</u> decreases the angle between
>   the bones; <u>extension</u> increases the angle: elbow joint.
>   <u>Sliding</u> <u>joint</u> (plane joint): intercarpal joints.
>   <u>Ball-and-socket</u> <u>joint</u> (spheroidal joint): hip joint.
>   <u>Pivot</u> <u>joint</u> (trochoid joint): atlantoaxial joint.
>   <u>Ellipsoid</u> <u>joint</u> (biaxial movement): antebrachiocarpal joint.

The initial swelling of an injured joint is due to increased production of synovial fluid. Analysis of the viscosity (thickness) of the synovial fluid and cells it contains is used to diagnose certain joint diseases.
Growth plate fractures occur in young colts.

Plate 13

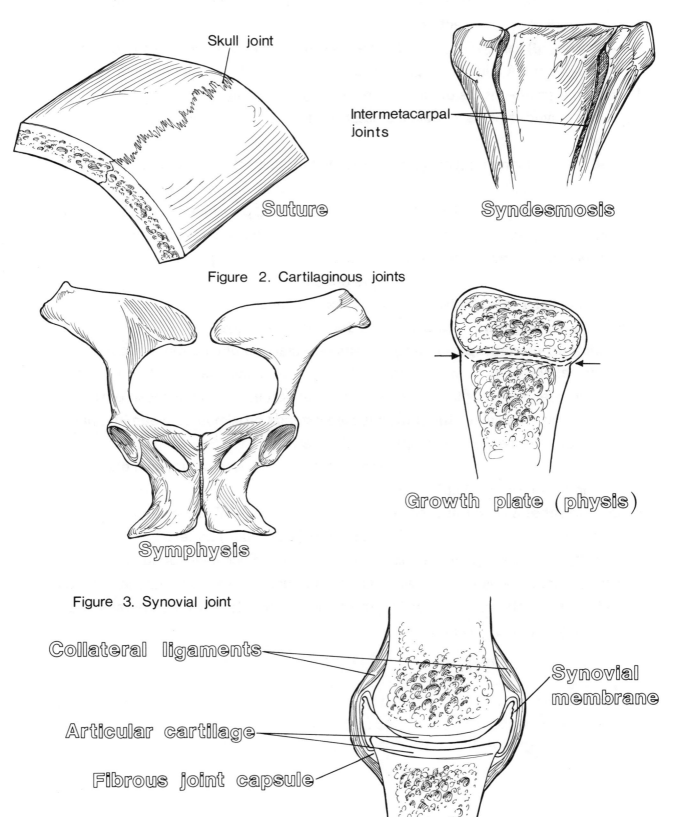

Figure 1. Fibrous joints

Skull joint

Suture

Intermetacarpal joints

Syndesmosis

Figure 2. Cartilaginous joints

Symphysis

Growth plate (physis)

Figure 3. Synovial joint

Collateral ligaments

Articular cartilage

Fibrous joint capsule

Synovial membrane

Shoulder (humeral) joint - Glenoid cavity of scapula and head of humerus. Surrounding muscles act as ligaments.

Elbow (cubital) joint - Condyle of humerus, proximal end of radius and trochlear notch of ulna. A thin joint capsule extends a pouch into the olecranon fossa.

Radioulnar joint - Shafts of radius and ulna. Interosseous ligament of the forearm forms a syndesmosis in foals that later ossifies distal to the interosseous foramen.

Carpal joints - Common collateral ligaments, fibrous joint capsule and palmar ligament

    Antebrachiocarpal joint - Distal end of radius and proximal row of carpal bones

    Midcarpal joint - Proximal row of carpal bones and distal row of carpal bones

    Carpometacarpal joint - Distal row of carpal bones and proximal ends of metacarpal bones

    Intercarpal joints - Between adjacent carpal bones

Intermetacarpal joints - Syndesmoses that ossify with age

Fetlock joint (metacarpophalangeal joint) - Distal end of third metacarpal bone, proximal end of proximal phalanx and the two proximal sesamoid bones. Several sesamoidean ligaments connect with and support the proximal sesamoid bones. The **palmar recess of the joint capsule** extends proximad between the third metacarpal bone and the suspensory ligament.

Proximal interphalangeal joint (pastern joint) - Distal end of proximal phalanx and proximal end of middle phalanx

Distal interphalangeal joint (coffin joint) - Distal end of middle phalanx, proximal end of distal phalanx and the distal sesamoid (navicular) bone

Wind-puffs are swellings of the palmar recess of the fetlock joint capsule. They are due to an excessive amount of synovial fluid produced by the synovial membrane of the fetlock joint. The condition occurs most commonly in hard-worked horses and may or may not result in lameness.

Plate 14

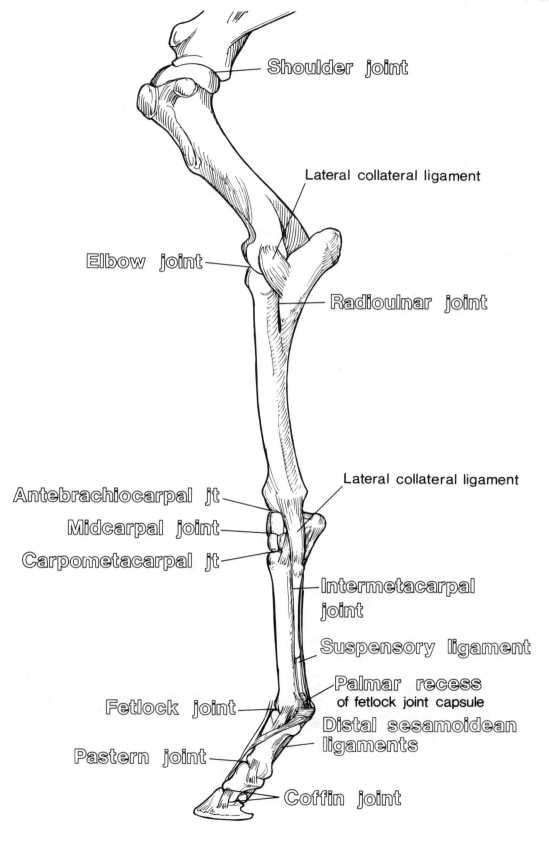

Shoulder joint

Lateral collateral ligament

Elbow joint

Radioulnar joint

Antebrachiocarpal jt
Midcarpal joint
Carpometacarpal jt

Lateral collateral ligament

Intermetacarpal joint

Suspensory ligament

Palmar recess
of fetlock joint capsule

Fetlock joint

Distal sesamoidean ligaments

Pastern joint

Coffin joint

Plate 15

FASCIA

The horse's fascia consists of layers of loose and dense fibrous (collagenous) connective tissue under the skin. Superficial fascia is loose collagenous connective tissue that blends with the same tissue of the subcutis. Superficial fascia covers deep fascia of dense collagenous connective tissue. When the skin, subcutis and superficial fascia are removed in most regions of the body, a covering of thick, white deep fascia masks many individual muscles from view. Deep fascia sends septa (partitions) between certain muscles or between their parts. Superficial and deep fascia also give attachment to some muscles. Cutaneous muscles are contained within superficial fascia. Major cutaneous muscles are the cutaneous trunk m. (flyshaker muscle), cutaneous facial m. and cutaneous neck m. Fascia covers joints and blends with ligaents and tendon sheaths.

MAJOR REGIONS OF DEEP FASCIA

Trunk

Abdominal fascia

Cervical fascia

Thoracolumbar fascia

> **Dorsoscapular ligament** - Attaches to vertebrae, scapula and muscles.

Forelimb

Antebrachial fascia

Omobrachial fascia

Hindlimb

Gluteal fascia

Crural fascia

Femoral fascia

Fascia lata

Carpal, metacarpal, tarsal, metatarsal and digital fasciae enclose their respective regions.

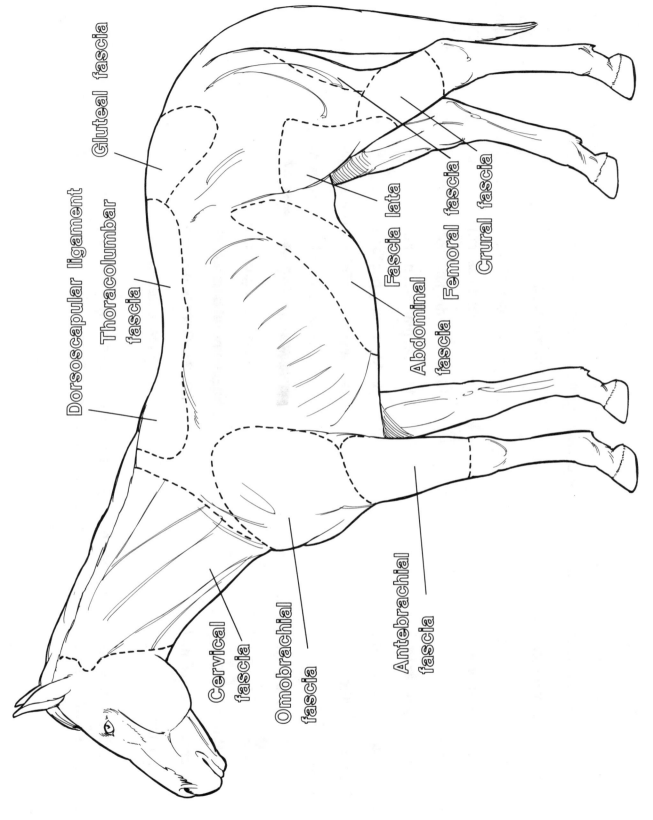

Dorsoscapular ligament

Thoracolumbar fascia

Gluteal fascia

Fascia lata

Abdominal fascia

Femoral fascia

Crural fascia

Cervical fascia

Omobrachial fascia

Antebrachial fascia

Plate 15

Plate 16

SUPERFICIAL MUSCLES OF THE HORSE

Muscles are named for their attachments, shapes, and/or actions. Only parts of some muscles are seen in this view. They will be seen more completely in a view of a deeper dissection. m.= muscle, mm.= muscles.

1. Superior labial levator m.

2. Canine m.

3. Nasolabial levator m.

4. Masseter m.

5. Sternomandibular m.

6. Cervical cutaneous m.

7. Brachiocephalic m.

8. Splenius m.

9. Cervical ventral serrated m.

10. Thoracic ventral serrated m.

11. Cervical trapezius m.

12. Thoracic trapezius m.

13. Subclavian m.

14. Deltoid m.

15. Latissimus dorsi m.

    (widest dorsal m.)

16. Descending pectoral m.

17. Brachial triceps m.

18. Ascending pectoral m.

19. Carpal and digital extensor mm.

20. External abdominal oblique m.

21. Tensor m. of the fascia lata

22. Superficial gluteal m.

23. Femoral biceps m.

24. Semitendinous m.

25. Digital extensor mm.

Acute and chronic muscle inflammation (myositis) are common problems in horses during and after strenuous exercise. Medication is available that modulates the body's immune system to deal with the swelling and pain of myositis.

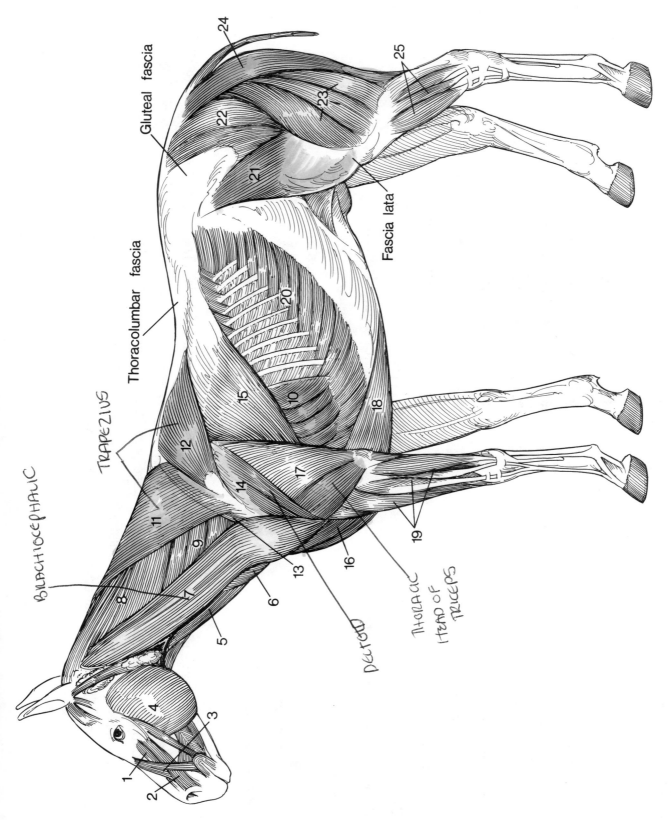

Gluteal fascia

Thoracolumbar fascia

TRAPEZIUS

BRACHIOCEPHALIC

Fascia lata

DELTOID

THORACIC
HEAD OF
TRICEPS

1
2
3
4
5
6
7
8
9
10
11
12
13
14
15
16
17
18
19
20
21
22
23
24
25

Plate 16

Plate 17

DEEPER MUSCLES OF THE HORSE

m. = muscle,   mm. = muscles

1. Longest capital and atlantal m.

2. Complex m.

3. Rhomboid m.

4. Thoracic spinal m.

5. Iliocostal m.

6. Longest dorsal m.

7. Caudal dorsal serrated m.

8. Omohyoid m.

9. Cervical ventral serrated m.

10. Thoracic ventral serrated m.

11. Subclavian m.

12. Supraspinate m.

13. Infraspinate m.

14. Brachial biceps m.

15. Long head of brachial triceps m.

16. Lateral head of brachial triceps m.

17. External intercostal mm.

18. Transverse abdominal m.

19. Internal abdominal oblique m.

20. External abdominal oblique m.

21. Iliac m.

22. Femoral quadriceps m.

23. Middle gluteal m.

24. Semimembranous m.

25. Semitendinous m.

26. Gastrocnemius m.

The tying-up syndrome is a muscular disease that follows prolonged, hard exercise. The condition occurs in certain horses apparently due to depletion of muscle energy. Affected horses are very stiff and do not want to move. They should not be forced to move! Electrolytes (salts) and glucose (simple sugar) given orally and intravenously have been used to treat tying-up. Injection of an immunomodulator has had dramatic results in alleviating tying-up syndrome. Prevention includes better conditioning, less strenuous exercise and giving the horse more water and extra electrolytes.

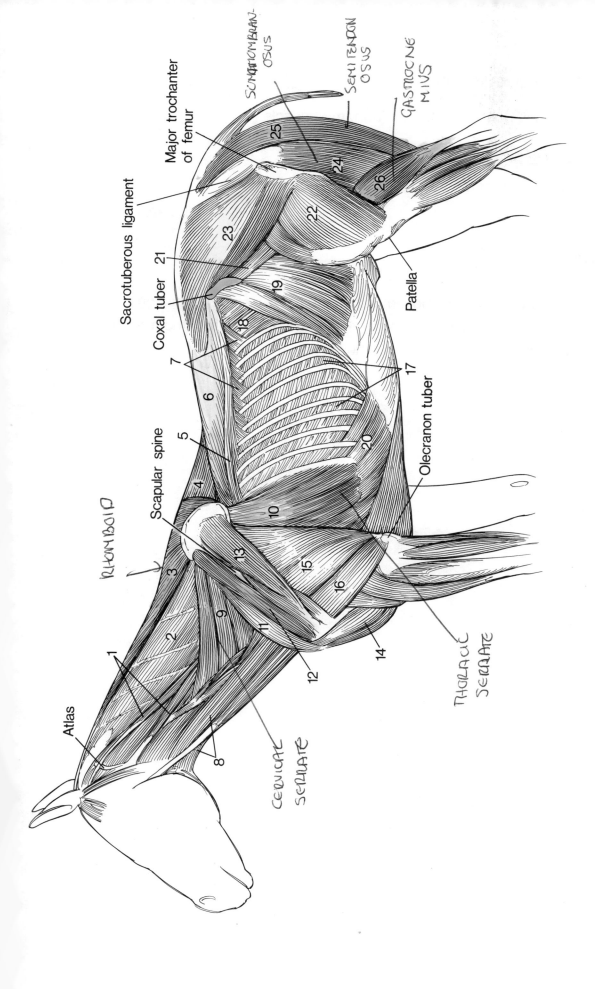

Atlas

RHOMBOID

Scapular spine

Sacrotuberous ligament

Major trochanter
of femur

Coxal tuber 21

7

6

5

4

3

13

9

11

8

CERVICAL
SERRATE

12

15

16

10

14

THORACIC
SERRATE

Olecranon tuber

Patella

SEMIMEMBRAN-
OSUS

SEMITENDIN
OSUS

GASTROCNE
MIUS

25

24

26

22

23

19

18

20

17

1

2

Plate 17

Plate 18

DEEP SHOULDER AND ARM MUSCLES

Medial view of dissected right shoulder and arm. m.= muscle

1. **Subscapular m.**
2. **Major teres m .**
3. **Tensor m. of antebrachial fascia**
4. **Coracobrachial m.**
5. **Medial head of brachial triceps m.**
6. **Brachial biceps m.**

In addition to flexion and extension, movements of the limbs include <u>adduction</u> - movement toward the median plane, <u>abduction</u> - movement away from the median plane, and a limited amount of <u>rotation</u> about the limb's axis.

Plate 18

Medial view

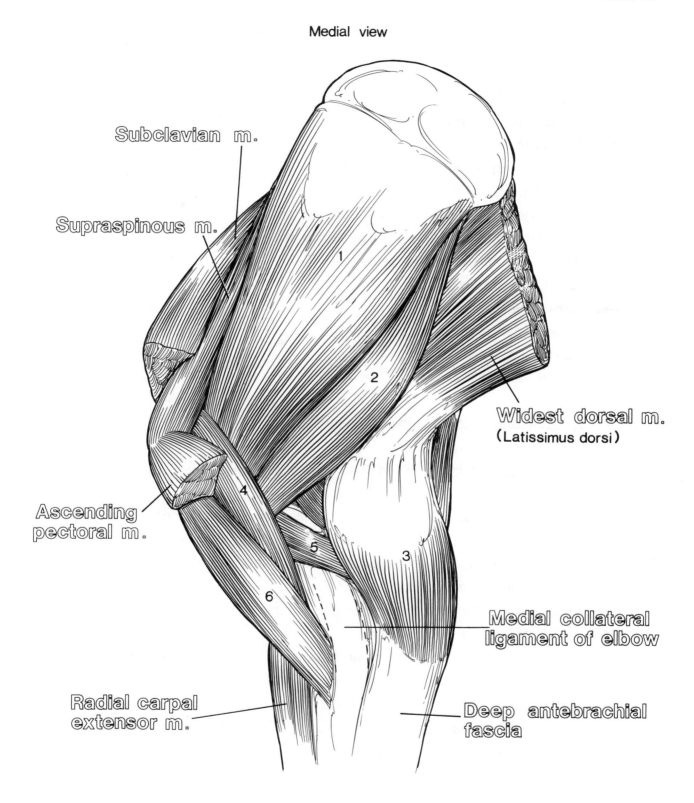

Subclavian m.

Supraspinous m.

Ascending
pectoral m.

Radial carpal
extensor m.

Widest dorsal m.
(Latissimus dorsi)

Medial collateral
ligament of elbow

Deep antebrachial
fascia

1

2

3

4

5

6

Right forelimb in flexion. m.= muscle
   1. Brachial m.
   2. Radial carpal extensor m.
   3. Common digital extensor m.
   4. Lateral digital extensor m.
   5. Lateral ulnar m.
   6. Ulnar head of deep digital flexor m.
   7. Oblique carpal extensor m.
   8. Superficial and deep digital flexor tendons
   9. Suspensory ligament (middle interosseous m.)
 10. Palmar anular ligament of the fetlock
 11. Proximal digital anular ligament
 12. Descending pectoral m.
 13. Transverse pectoral m.
 14. Radial carpal flexor m.
 15. Ulnar carpal flexor m.

Color the synovial tendon sheaths indicated by stippled regions.

A smooth palmar carpal ligament fills in the irregular surface of the palmar aspects
of the carpal bones.
A fibrous **flexor retinaculum** stretches from the accessory carpal bone to the medial
collateral ligament and proximal end of the second metacarpal bone, forming the
carpal canal. The carpal and digital flexor tendons, vessels and nerves are embedded in the connective tissue of the carpal canal.
The fibrous **extensor retinaculum** holds carpal and digital extensor tendons in
place.
The palmar anular ligament of the fetlock and the proximal digital anular ligament
enclose and support the digital flexor tendons.
The superficial digital flexor tendon, which functions to resist downward motion,
responds to exercise by enlarging. Thickening caused by inflammation (tendonitis) of
a flexor tendon is commonly called bowed tendon. It occurs most frequently in the
superficial digital flexor tendon.

Plate 19

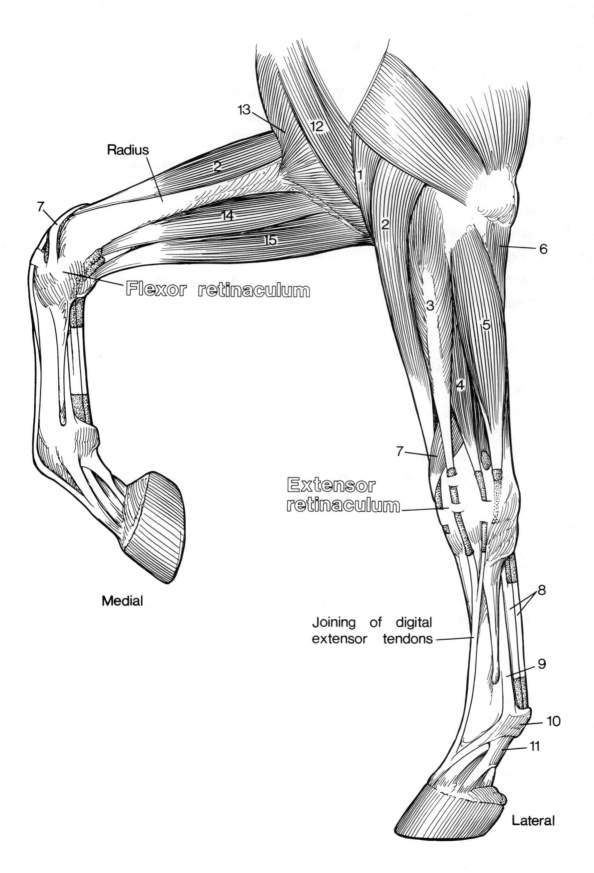

Radius

Flexor retinaculum

Medial

Extensor retinaculum

Joining of digital extensor tendons

Lateral

Figure 1. Lateral view of a dissection of the left withers. The trapezius muscle has been removed. The **thoracic rhomboid muscle** and **nuchal ligament** have been pulled away from the superficial surface of the **dorsoscapular ligament,** a thickened part of the thoracolumbar fascia that helps to attach the trunk to the shoulder. The dorsal part (seen here) arises from the spines of T3, T4 and T5 vertebrae. Elastic bands from the ventral part (not seen here) attach to the medial surface of the **scapula** between attachments of the **ventral serrated muscles.** Identify and color the dorsoscapular ligament (outlined by a dashed line and over the thoracic spines) and the structures associated with it.

1. **Supraspinous bursa**
2. **Rhomboid muscle**
3. **Capital semispinal muscle**

4. **Splenius muscle**
5,5'. **Ventral serrated muscles**
6. **Dorsal serrated muscle**

Fistulous withers or sinus of the withers is an infection of the **supraspinous bursa** draining into the region of the **dorsoscapular ligament** and associated fascial planes and eventually breaking through to the surface of the withers.

Figure 2. Lateral view of dissected **nuchal ligament. The funicular part of the nuchal ligament** consists of two parallel cords that attach to the skull and flatten caudally where they merge with the **supraspinous ligament.** Elastic bands of the **lamellar part** extend from the funicular part and the second and third thoracic spines to spines of the axis and C3 to C5 or C6.

Elasticity of the nuchal ligament minimizes muscular exertion when the horse lowers or raises its head during grazing.

Poll evil is an infection of the **cranial nuchal (atlantal) bursa** and related structures.

Plate 20

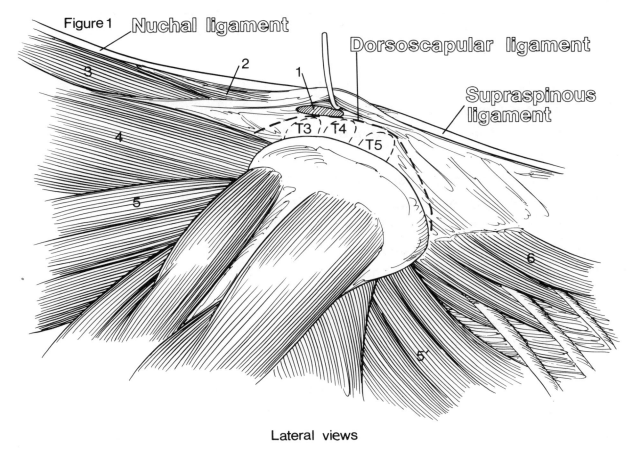

Figure 1

Nuchal ligament

Dorsoscapular ligament

Supraspinous ligament

3

2

1

T3 T4 T5

4

5

6

5'

Lateral views

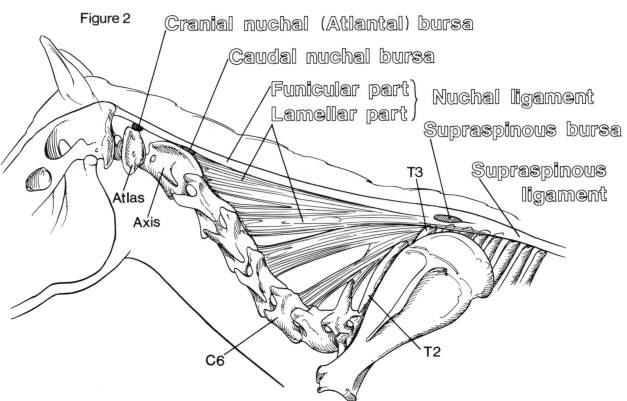

Figure 2

Cranial nuchal (Atlantal) bursa

Caudal nuchal bursa

Funicular part }
Lamellar part } Nuchal ligament

Supraspinous bursa

Supraspinous ligament

T3

Atlas

Axis

C6

T2

Tendons are indicated by dashed or dotted lines. Parts of some tendons pass through muscles.

1. **Tendons of the brachial biceps muscle**
2. **Fascial covering and tendon of radial carpal extensor muscle**
3. **Tendon of common digital extensor muscle**
4. **Thoracic serrated muscle**
5. **Long head of brachial triceps muscle**
6. **Radial check ligament of superficial digital flexor muscle**
7. **Tendon of superficial digital flexor muscle**
8. **Carpal check ligament of deep digital flexor muscle**
9. **Tendon of deep digital flexor muscle**
10. **Suspensory ligament**
11. **Extensor branch of suspensory ligament**
12. **Three distal sesamoidean ligaments**

Stabilization of the joints of the forelimb by ligaments and tendons of the stay apparatus with a minimum of muscular activity permits the horse to stand while sleeping. Continuous tendons of the brachial biceps and radial carpal extensor prevent flexion of the shoulder joint, and muscular tension of the long head of the brachial triceps m. prevents flexion of the elbow and collapse of the forelimb. The carpus is stabilized by the shape of the carpal bones, the palmar carpal ligament, the digital flexor tendons in the carpal canal, and the carpal and digital extensor tendons. Overextension of the fetlock is prevented by the suspensory ligament, the proximal sesamoid bones and the ligaments surrounding them, and the three distal sesamoidean ligaments. The superficial digital flexor tendon extends from the radius by its radial check ligament, ending on the proximal phalanx. The carpal check ligament continues distad from the palmar carpal ligament to join the deep digital flexor tendon in the middle of the metacarpus. The tendon then pierces the superficial digital flexor tendon, goes over the palmar surface of the fetlock and continues distad to pass over the navicular bone and insert on the distal phalanx.

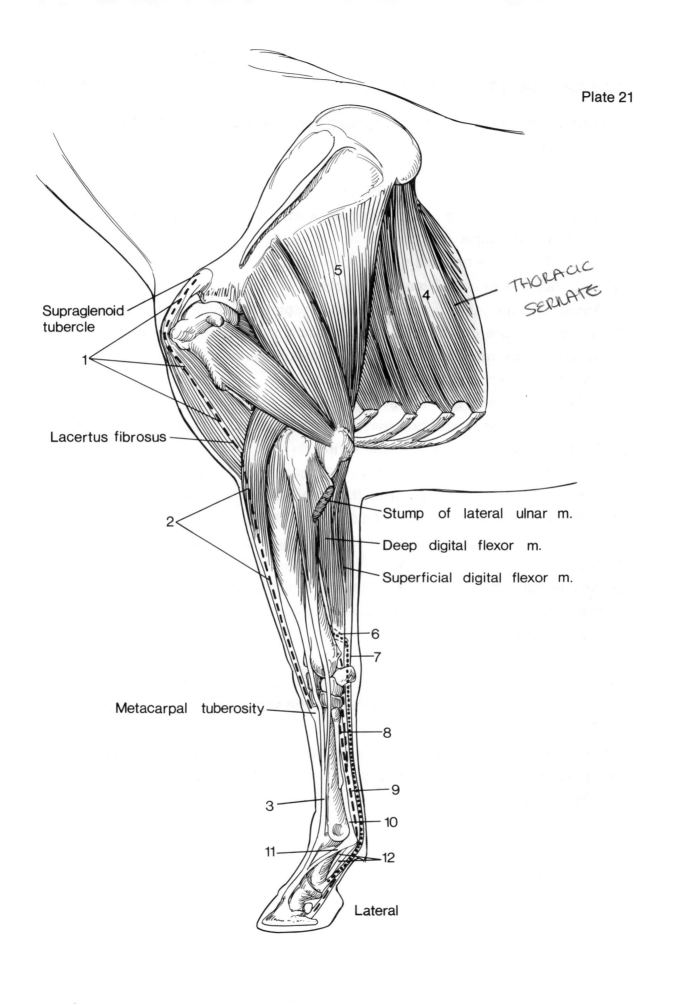

Plate 21

Supraglenoid
tubercle

1

Lacertus fibrosus

2

5

4

THORACIC
SERRATE

Stump of lateral ulnar m.

Deep digital flexor m.

Superficial digital flexor m.

6

7

Metacarpal   tuberosity

8

9

3

10

11

12

Lateral

Forelimb nerves come from the brachial plexus, a network of ventral branches from the last three cervical and first two thoracic spinal nerves.

Underline the names of the nerves in different colors and trace the course of each nerve indicated by the numbers in the same color. n.= nerve.

Figure 1. Mediocaudal view of left forelimb skeleton with courses of the nerves
                drawn roughly upon it.

Figure 2. Lateral view of left forelimb showing cutaneous sensory nerves.

 1. **Subscapular n.** - to subscapular muscle

 2. **Suprascapular n.** - around scapula to supraspinate and infraspinate muscles

 3. **Musculocutaneous n.** - to pectoral muscles and flexor muscles of the shoulder

3a. **Medial cutaneous antebrachial n.** - from 3, sensory to skin

 4. **Median n.** - to carpal and digital flexor muscles

 5. **Ulnar n.** - to carpal and digital flexor muscles

5a. **Caudal cutaneous antebrachial n.** - from 5, sensory to skin

5b. **Dorsal branch of ulnar n.** - sensory to skin

 6. **Radial n.** - to extensor muscles of elbow, carpus and digit

6a. **Lateral cutaneous antebrachial n.** - from 6, sensory to skin

 7. **Axillary n.** - to flexor muscles of shoulder

7a. **Cranial cutaneous antebrachial n.** - from 7, sensory to skin

 8. **Medial palmar n.**

 9. **Lateral palmar n.**   } Primarily

10. **Communicating branch**   } sensory

11. **Medial palmar digital n.**   } nerves

12. **Dorsal branch of 11.**

A nerve block (local anesthesia) is performed for surgery or to diagnose a site of pain.

"Nerving" refers to cutting a palmar (or plantar) digital nerve to relieve pain.

"Sweeney", atrophy (shrinkage) of supraspinate and infraspinate muscles, is due to injury to the suprascapular nerve.

Plate 22

Figure 1

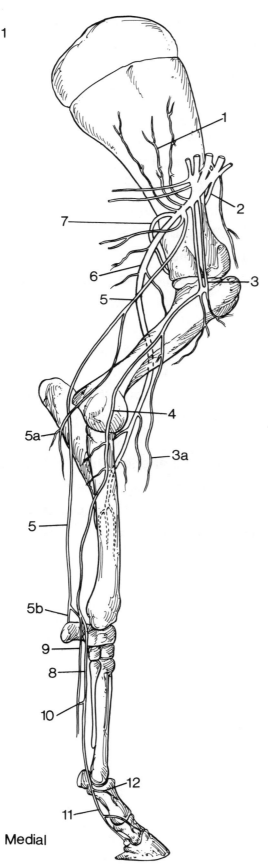

Medial

Figure 2

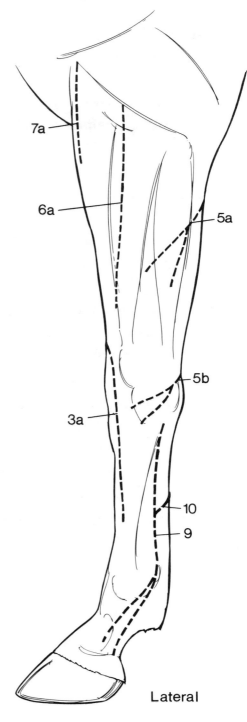

Lateral

Color the courses of the vessels indicated. Red is usually used for arteries; blue, for veins. Dashed lines trace vessels on the opposite side of the limb in these medial views. a.= artery; aa.= arteries; v.= vein; vv.= veins

<u>Major</u> <u>Arteries</u>   <u>Major</u> <u>Veins</u>

Major Arteries	Major Veins
1. **Suprascapular a.**	9. **Suprascapular v.**
2. **Subscapular a.**	10. **Subscapular v.**
3. **Thoracodorsal a.**	11. **Thoracodorsal v.**
4. **External thoracic a.**	12. **External thoracic v.**
5. **Deep brachial a.**	("spur vein")
6. **Bicipital a.**	13. **Deep brachial v.**
7. **Cranial interosseous a.**	14. **Bicipital v.**
8. **Med. and lat. palmar metacarpal aa.**	Med. and lat. palmar metacarpal vv. not shown.

Blood reaching the foot flows primarily through the following sequence of arteries: **axillary - brachial - median - medial palmar** (common digital) - **medial and lateral digital aa.** The two digital aa. meet to form the **terminal arch** within the solar canal of the distal phalanx. Branches from the terminal arch run through the distal phalanx.

Whereas most veins are <u>satellites</u> (companions) of the arteries, there are some differences between the venous drainage of the forelimb and its arterial supply. Notice the <u>two</u> **median veins, the median cubital vein** and the **cephalic vein.** Blood is forced from the foot by concussive pressure on a complex of <u>venous plexuses</u> (networks).

Veins differ from arteries in that they:
    a. contain a larger volume of blood,
    b. have thinner walls,
    c. and usually have <u>valves</u>, the <u>cusps</u> of which direct blood toward the heart.

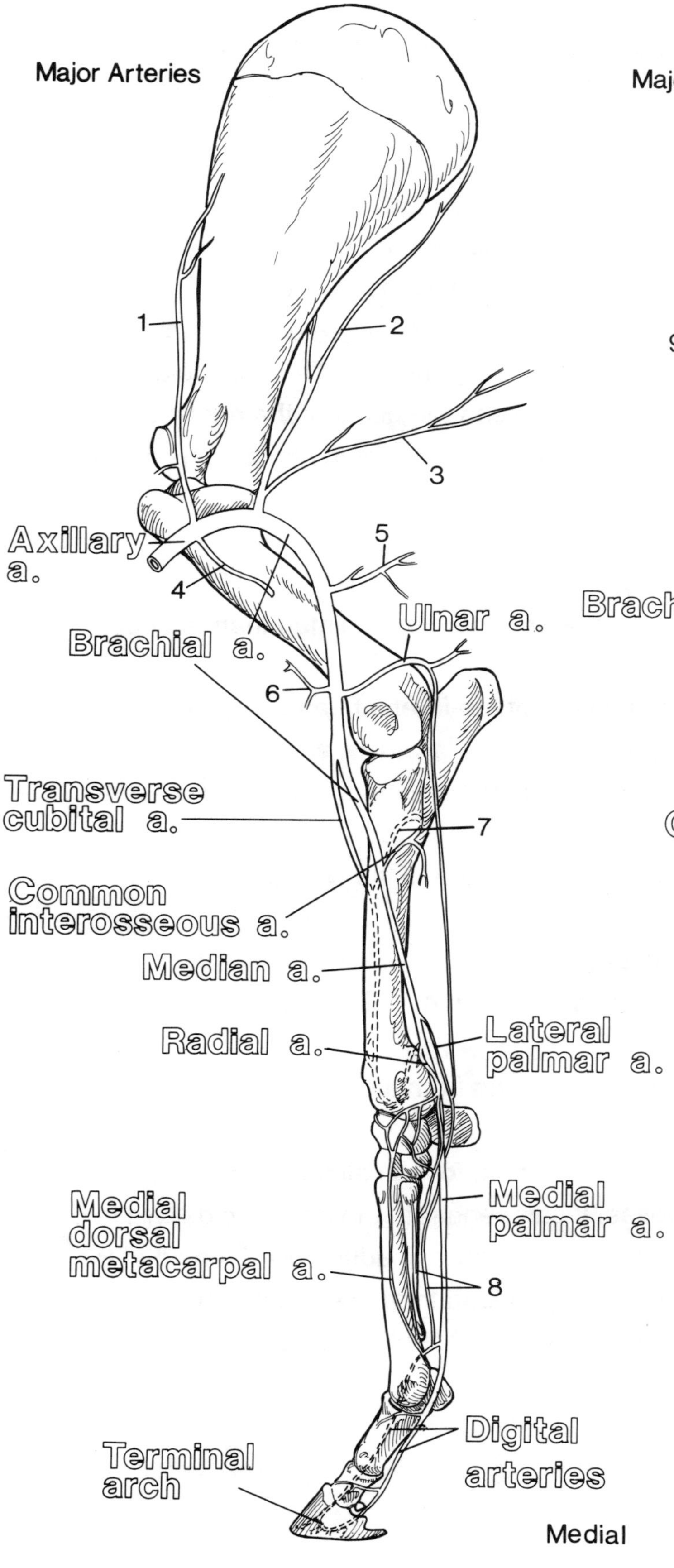

Plate 23

Major Arteries

Major Veins

1

2

3

Axillary a.

4

5

Ulnar a.

Brachial a.

6

Transverse cubital a.

7

Common interosseous a.

Median a.

Radial a.

Lateral palmar a.

Medial dorsal metacarpal a.

Medial palmar a.

8

Terminal arch

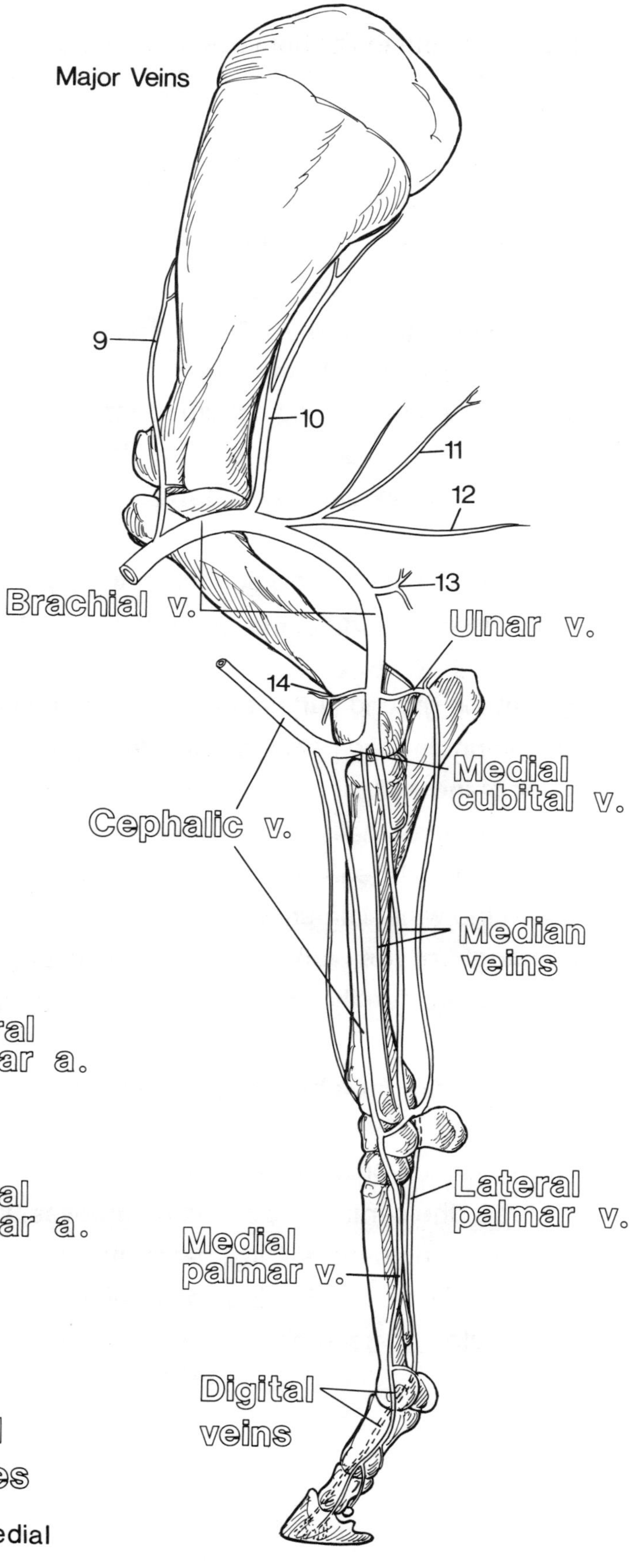

Digital arteries

Medial

9

10

11

12

Brachial v.

13

Ulnar v.

14

Cephalic v.

Medial cubital v.

Median veins

Medial palmar v.

Lateral palmar v.

Digital veins

Figure 1. Side of the hoof

Coronet	**Toe**	Regions
Skin	**Quarter**	of the
Periople	**Heel**	hoof wall

The **coronet** is the junction of the skin and the soft horn of the **periople.** The coronary band is a deeper region. Notice that the **periople** widens over the **heel.**
Hoof and foot are not the same! The hoof (like your fingernail) is a highly cornified (horny) epidermal structure lacking in blood vessels and nerves. The foot includes the hoof and underlying corium (dermis), skin between the bulbs of the heels, digital cushion, distal phalanx and its cartilages, distal end of the middle phalanx, navicular bone, coffin joint, ligaments, tendons, vessels and nerves.

Figure 2. Ground (solar) surface of the hoof
Notice that the hoof of the hindfoot, B., is narrower and more pointed than the hoof of the forefoot, A.
Half of the ground surface of the wall of the hoof of the forefoot has been trimmed. On the untrimmed half, the **epidermal ("insensitive") laminae, el,** of the **internal layer** of the wall blend with the thick **middle layer.** These layers may also be seen on the trimmed half.
Identify the **white line,** the soft white horn at the junction of the wall and the sole. Leave the white line uncolored.
The **angle of the wall** continues into the **bar.**
On the **frog** identify the **apex,** a., and the **central groove,** c. The **frog** blends with the **bulbs of the heels.**
On each side, a **collateral groove** separates the frog from the bar and the sole.

Thrush is a chronic infection of the frog in which dark, foul-smelling dead tissue occurs in the central and collateral grooves. It can penetrate the horny epidermis into the underlying dermis. Dirty, damp stables and paddocks, inadequate cleaning of the hoof, and improper shoeing and hoof trimming can lead to thrush. A bacterium, Fusobacterium necrophorum, is usually present in the affected tissues.

Plate 24

Figure 1

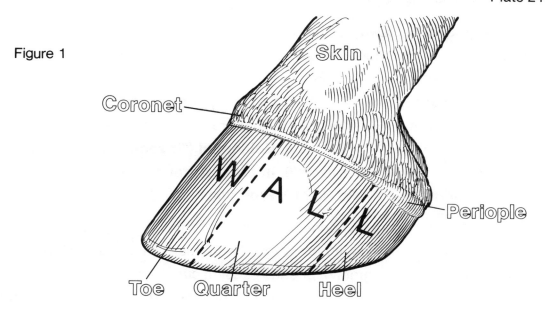

Skin

Coronet

W A L L

Periople

Toe   Quarter   Heel

Figure 2

Angle of the wall

Bar

White line
Internal layer
Middle layer

c
Frog
a

S O L E

el

Untrimmed   Trimmed

A. Hoof of the forefoot

Bulbs of the heels

Collateral
groove

c
Frog
a

S O L E

B. Hoof of the hindfoot

Figure 1. Hoof pulled away from underlying corium.

Adjacent regions of corium (dermis) and hoof (epidermis):

1. **Perioplic corium** - - - - fits into 6. **Perioplic groove**

2. **Coronary corium** - - - - fits into 7. **Coronary groove**

3. **Laminar corium** - - - - - **dermal ("sensitive") laminae** interlock with

                                     8. **Epidermal ("insensitive") laminae of wall**

4. **Corium of sole** - - - fits against 9. **Internal surface of sole**

5. **Corium of frog** - - - - - fits over 10. **Frog stay**

The **corium** is collagenous connective tissue containing many nourishing blood vessels and nerve endings. It blends into the periosteum of the distal phalanx. Over-eating in lush pastures, grain overloads causing circulation of endotoxins (poisons) and hard concussion on the foot may cause blood to be shunted away from small arteries in dermal laminae, resulting in <u>laminitis</u> (<u>founder</u>). Shunting of blood from dermal laminae at first causes swelling and then death of tissue possibly followed by loosening and downward rotation of the distal phalanx.

Figure 2. Growth of the hoof. The stippled line from **1 to 1'** indicates the layer of **basal epidermal cells** that proliferate (multiply) to <u>form</u> <u>the</u> <u>hoof</u>. The dashed line from **2 to 2'** indicates the underlying **dermis**.

 A. higher magnification of:

       3. **papillae (projections) of coronary corium** covered by

       4. **basal cells of the coronary epidermis.**

          Epidermal cells over the papillae form -

       5. **horn tubules;** epidermal cells in between form -

       6. **intertubular horn.**

          Tubular and intertubular horn move toward the ground, forming the

       7. **middle layer of the hoof wall.** The cells cornify (become horny) as they

          are pushed toward the ground.

Arrow indicates direction of growth: <u>1/4 to 1/2 inch per month</u>.

Notice **8, interlocking of dermal and epidermal laminae,** then go to B. Higher magnification of:

       9. **Dermal lamina.** Notice the small blood vessels.

      10. **Epidermal lamina.** Cells not yet cornified.

Plate 25

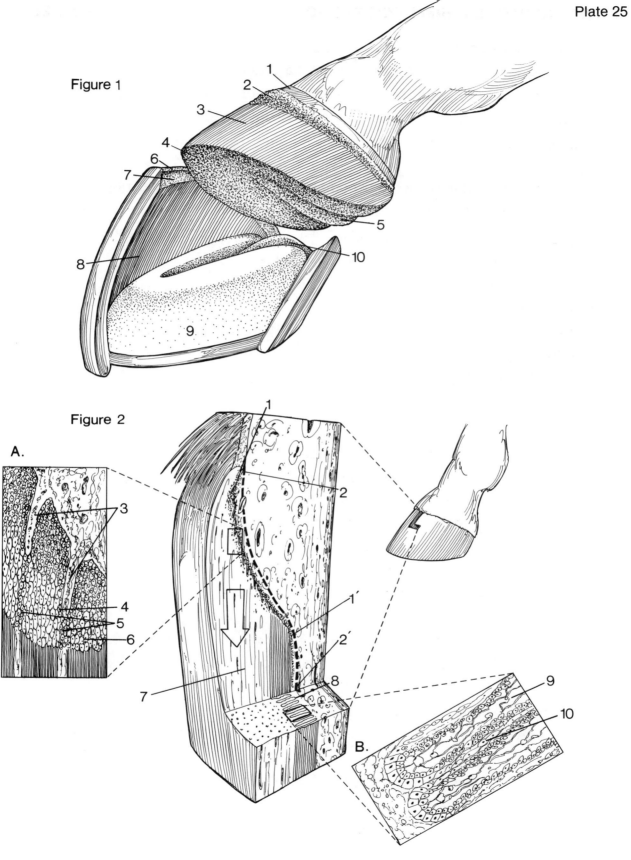

Figure 1

Figure 2

A.

B.

1. Lateral palmar nerve
2. Lateral palmar vein
3. Lateral palmar metacarpal nerve
4. Lateral palmar digital nerve
5. Dorsal branch of 4.

6. Lateral digital artery
7. Lateral digital vein
8. Ligament of the ergot
9. Coronary venous plexus

Notice that the lateral palmar nerve becomes the lateral palmar digital nerve. The vessels follow a similar sequence. Vessels and nerves on the medial side are distributed and named the same, substituting medial for lateral. A complex system of venous sinuses and veins drain into the digital veins.

The **ligament of the ergot** must be distinguished from the **lateral (or medial) palmar digital nerve** in the "nerving" operation (neurectomy). In this procedure a small piece of the nerve is cut out to relieve pain in the caudal part of the foot, particularly in the region of the navicular bone.

Plate 26

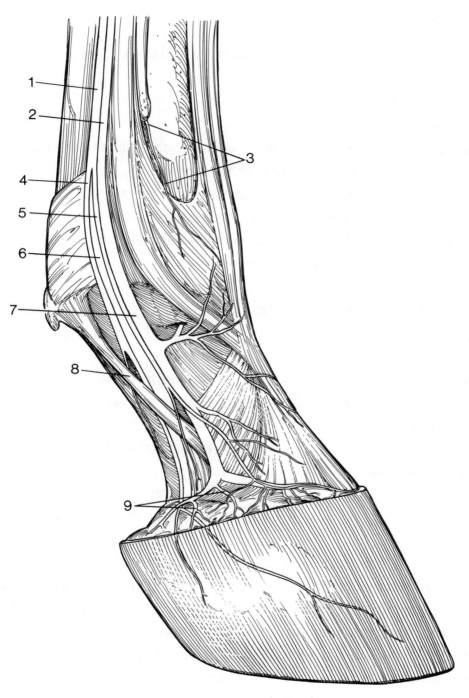

1
2
3
4
5
6
7
8
9

Lateral

Figure 1. Insertion of deep digital flexor tendon. Palmar view. Identify and color the following structures:

> **Deep digital flexor tendon**
> **Navicular bone**
> **Collateral sesamoidean ligament**   Meets opposite ligament - dashed line.
> **Navicular bursa** (podotrochlear bursa) - stippled

Notice the course of the deep digital flexor tendon over the navicular bone with the navicular bursa forming a cushion between the tendon and the navicular bone. Identify the dashed line indicating the outline of the navicular bone and the dotted line indicating the extent of the navicular bursa.

Figure 2. Parasagittal section through the digit.

1.- 1'. Limits of digital sheath
2. Palmar recess of fetlock joint capsule
3. Proximal sesamoid bone
4. Distal sesamoidean ligaments
5. Superficial digital flexor tendon
6. Deep digital flexor tendon
7. T ligament
8. Proximal pouch of coffin joint capsule
9. Navicular bone
10. Digital cushion
11. Navicular bursa
12. Impar ligament of navicular bone
13. Dorsal pouch of coffin joint capsule
14. Common digital extensor tendon

Navicular disease is a progressive, degenerative condition of the navicular bone, also affecting the navicular bursa and overlying deep digital flexor tendon. This condition occurs mainly in the forefeet. Upright conformation of the digit, small feet, improper shoeing, exercise on a hard surface, and very demanding work are thought to cause and aggravate the condition. Off and on lameness and shifting and pointing of the forefeet are common signs of the disease.

Plate 27

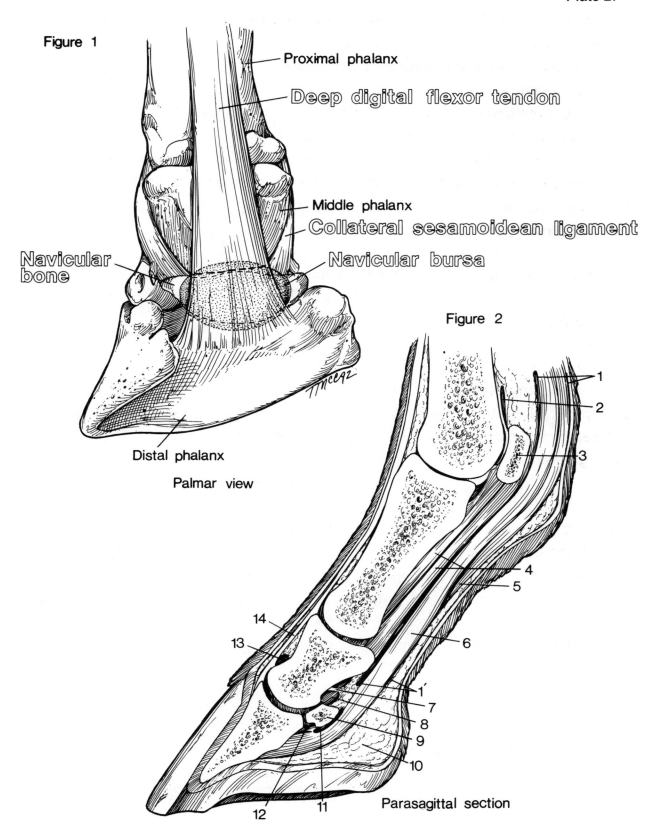

Figure 1

Proximal phalanx

Deep digital flexor tendon

Middle phalanx

Collateral sesamoidean ligament

Navicular bursa

Navicular bone

Distal phalanx

Palmar view

Figure 2

1
2
3
4
5
6
14
13
1'
7
8
9
10
12
11

Parasagittal section

Bones of the pelvic girdle:

ilium, pubis, ischium, sacrum, caudal vertebrae

Identify and color the following parts of the bones:

1. **Coxal tuber**
2. **Crest of ilium**
3. **Sacral tuber**
4. **Pubic tubercles**
5. **Ischiadic spine**
6. **Acetabulum**
7. **Obturator foramen**
8. **Symphysis pelvis**
9. **Ischiadic tuber**

Plate 28

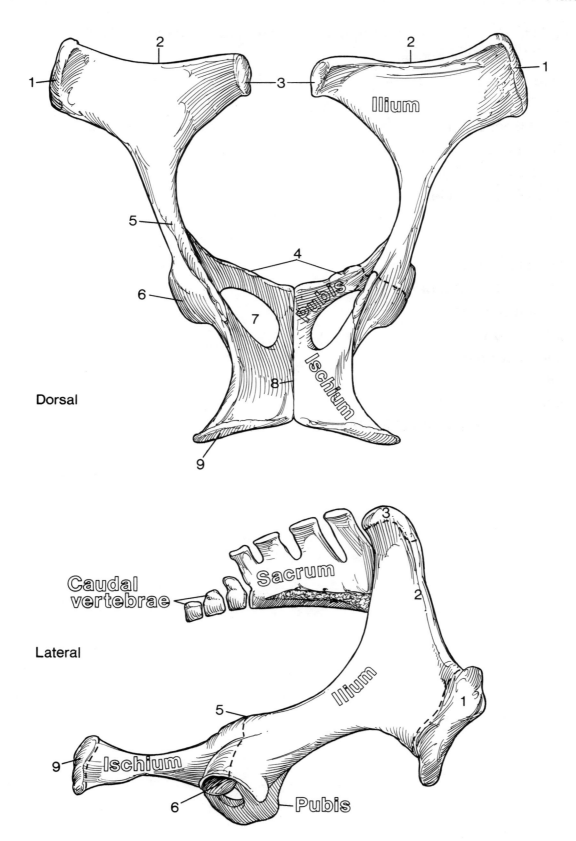

Dorsal

Lateral

Bones of the thigh and leg: **femur, patella, tibia, fibula.** Identify and color the following parts of the bones:

1. **Major (greater) trochanter**
2. **Head**
3. **Third trochanter**
4. **Minor (lesser) trochanter**
5. **Lateral epicondyle**
6. **Medial epicondyle**
7. **Trochlea**
8. **Lateral condyle**
9. **Medial condyle**
10. **Intercondylar eminence**
11. **Tibial tuberosity**
12. **Lateral condyle**
13. **Medial condyle**
14. **Lateral malleolus**
15. **Medial malleolus**
16. **Articular surface (tibial cochlea)**

Plate 29

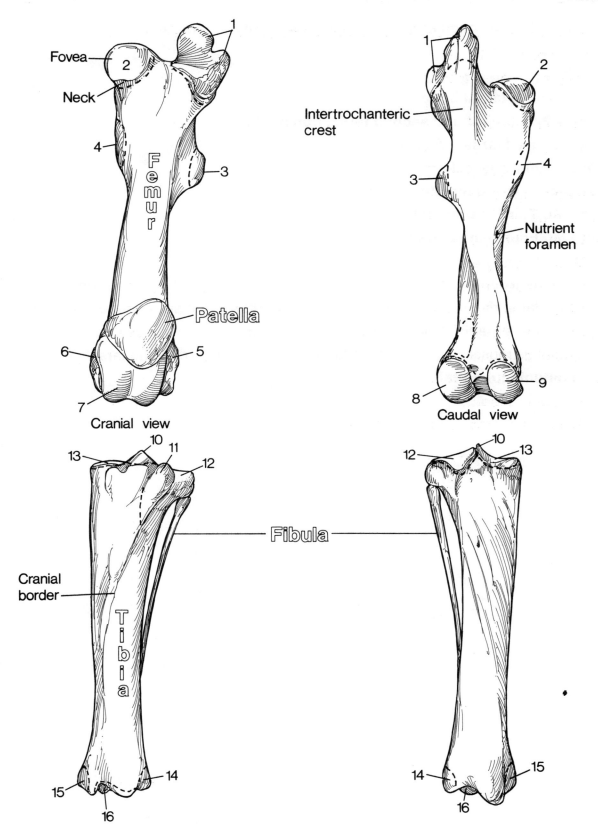

Fovea

Neck

4

Femur

3

Patella

6

5

7

Cranial view

Intertrochanteric crest

Nutrient foramen

8

9

Caudal view

13   10   11   12

Cranial border   Tibia

Fibula

14

15

16

12   10   13

Fibula

14   15

16

BONES OF THE HOCK **Plate 30**

Identify the **tarsal bones** and proximal ends of the **metatarsal bones**.

C. Calcaneus

T. Talus

CT. Central tarsal bone

1st & 2nd T. First and second tarsal bones - fused

3rd T. Third tarsal bone

4th T. Fourth tarsal bone

2nd Mt. Second metatarsal bone

3rd Mt. Third metatarsal bone

4th Mt. Fourth metatarsal bone

Ridges of the **trochlea** of the talus articulate with the two oblique grooves on the distal articular surface of the tibia. The **calcaneal tuber** is the site of attachment for tendons of the superficial digital flexor, gastrocnemius, femoral biceps and semitendinous muscles. The deep digital flexor tendon plays over the tarsal groove in the **sustentaculum tali.**

Plate 30

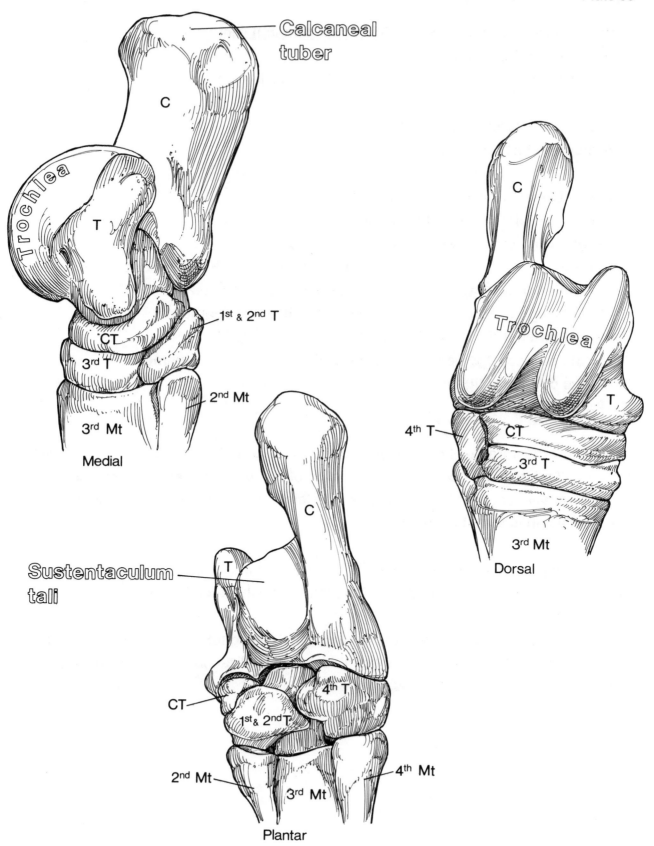

Calcaneal tuber

Trochlea

C

T

1st & 2nd T

CT

3rd T

2nd Mt

3rd Mt

Medial

Sustentaculum tali

C

T

CT

4th T

1st & 2nd T

2nd Mt

3rd Mt

4th Mt

Plantar

C

Trochlea

T

4th T

CT

3rd T

3rd Mt

Dorsal

Figure 1. Ventromedial view of right hip (<u>coxofemoral</u>) joint.

1. Symphysial ligament

2. Accessory femoral ligament (Only in the horse family)

3. Ligament of the head of the femur

4. Transverse acetabular ligament

5. Attachment of joint capsule

Figure 2. Cranial view of right stifle joint.

Figure 3. Medial view of right stifle joint.

<u>Stifle</u> <u>joint</u> = <u>femoropatellar</u> joint + <u>femorotibial</u> <u>joint</u>.

1. Patella	**8. Lateral femoropatellar ligament**
2. Parapatellar cartilage	**9. Lateral patellar ligament**
3. Medial ridge of trochlea	**10. Lateral collateral ligament**
4. Medial patellar ligament	**11. Lateral meniscus**
5. Middle patellar ligament	**12. Medial femoropatellar ligament**
6. Medial collateral ligament	**13. Medial meniscus**
7. Tibial tuberosity	

Notice how the parapatellar cartilage and medial patellar ligament can move up over the medial ridge of the trochlea as contraction of the femoral quadriceps muscle pulls the patella proximad in extension of the femorotibial joint. In some conditions the patella can lock at the highest point.

The medial and lateral menisci (singular = meniscus) are C-shaped plates of fibrocartilage between the condyles of the femur and those of the tibia.

Crossed <u>cranial</u> and <u>caudal</u> <u>cruciate</u> <u>ligaments</u> extending from the femur to the tibia in the middle of the femorotibial joint contribute to stabilization of the joint. They are named for their tibial attachments.

Plate 31

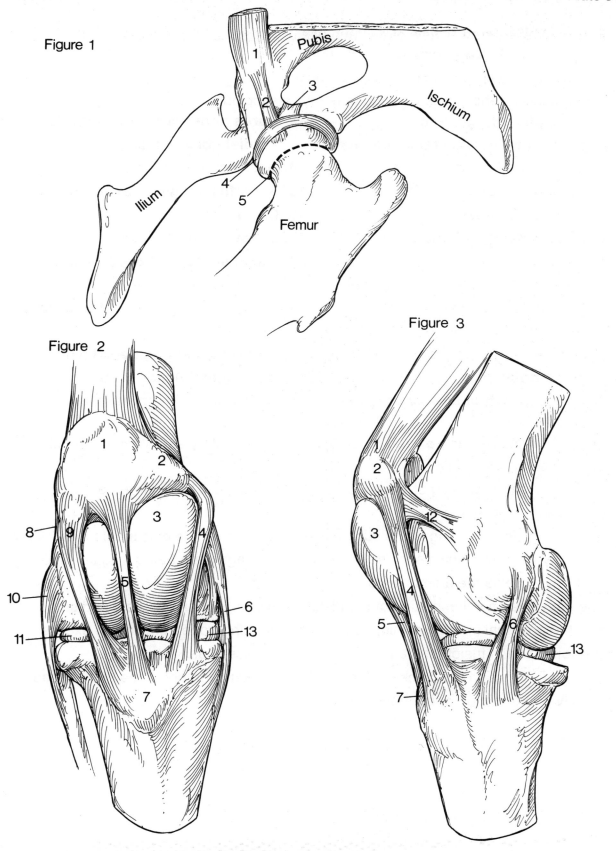

Figure 1

Pubis

Ischium

Ilium

Femur

Figure 2

Figure 3

Figure 1. Lateral view of dissected right hock.
Figure 2. Dorsal view of dissected right hock.
Figure 3. Medial view of dissected right hock.
Joint capsules, tendon sheaths and bursae are stippled.

1. **Long plantar ligament**
2. **Short lateral collateral ligament**
3. **Long lateral collateral ligament**
4. **Proximal intertarsal joint**
5. **Distal intertarsal joint**
6. **Tarsometatarsal joint**
7. **Tarsocrural joint**
8. **Short medial collateral ligament**
9. **Long medial collateral ligament**
10. **Dorsal tarsal ligament**
11. **Cranial branch of medial saphenous vein**
12. **Dorsal pouch of tarsocrural joint**
13. **Bursa under cunean tendon (of cranial tibial muscle)**
14. **Gastrocnemius tendon**
15. **Superficial digital flexor tendon**
16. **Calcaneal bursa**
17. **Subcutaneous bursa**
18. **Tarsal sheath - of deep digital flexor tendon**
19. **Medioplantar pouch of tarsocrural joint**
20. **Tendon sheath of medial head of deep digital flexor muscle (long digital flexor muscle)**

Synovial structures can be seen or felt (palpated) when they are inflamed and filled with excess synovial fluid.

Bog spavin is the swelling of the tarsocrural joint capsule. The enlarged dorsal pouch is particularly noticeable.

Capped hock is a swelling of the subcutaneous bursa over the calcaneal tuber (17) caused by repeated blows such as those from kicks against a trailer tailgate. This bursa develops as the animal ages.

Bone spavin is an inflammation of the distal intertarsal, tarsometatarsal and some-times the proximal intertarsal joints and the surrounding bone, resulting in excess bone formation. If fusion of the joints occurs, lameness usually stops.

Curb is inflammation and thickening of the long plantar ligament. It may be caused by faulty conformation or by repeated blows.

Plate 32

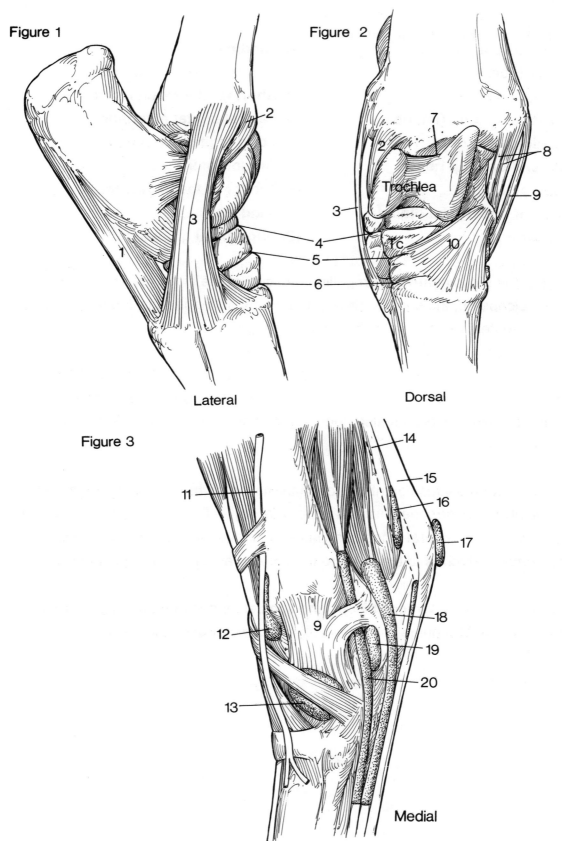

Figure 1

2

3

1

4
5

6

Lateral

Figure 2

7

2

Trochlea

3

Tc

8

9

10

Dorsal

Figure 3

11

12

13

14

15

16

17

9

18

19

20

Medial

Left hindlimb.

1. **Semitendinous m.**
2. **Femoral biceps m.**
   (three divsions)
3. **Gastrocnemius m. (lat. head)**
4. **Deep digital flexor m.**
   (lateral or deep head)
4'. **Tendon of 4**
5. **Tendon of superficial digital**
   flexor m.
6. **Middle interosseous m.**
   (suspensory ligament)
7. **Short digital extensor m.**
8. **Lateral digital extensor m.**
9. **Long digital extensor m.**
9'. **Tendon of 9**
10. **Tensor of fascia lata m.**
11. **Middle gluteal m.**
12. **Superficial gluteal m.**

Extensors of the hip joint are the propelling muscles of the hindlimb. They are part of the femoral biceps m., the semitendinous m. and, most importantly, the large mass of the middle gluteal m. that gives the rump its shape.

Flexors of the hip joint seen laterally include the tensor of the facia lata and the superficial gluteal muscles. The latter muscle along with the middle and deep gluteals and the femoral biceps also abduct (move away from the midline) the hindlimb.

Tendons from four muscles contribute to the formation of the **common calcaneal tendon,** mainly the gastrocnemius and superficial digital flexor tendons with smaller tendons from the the femoral biceps and semitendinous muscles. The common calcaneal tendon attaches to the calcaneal tuber and acts to extend the hock joint.

The groove between the femoral biceps and semitendinous muscles is seen readily on the living horse. The bulge of the long digital extensor can also be seen.

Plate 33

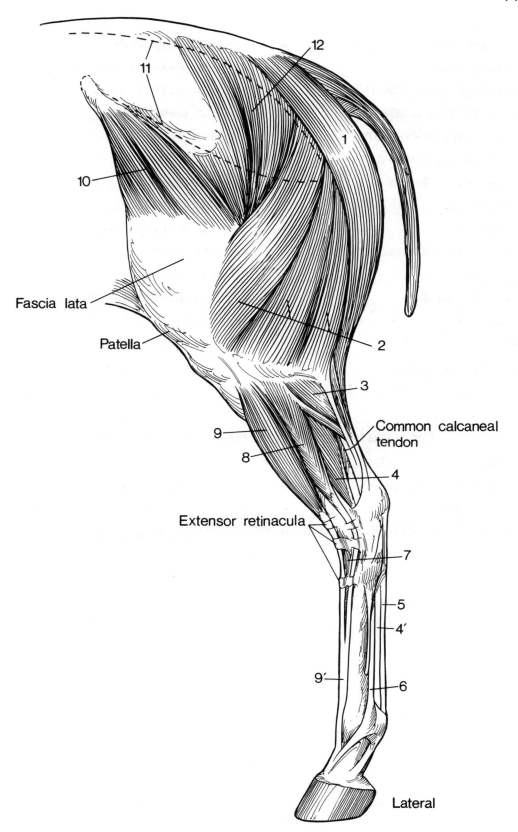

11

12

10

1

Fascia lata

Patella

2

3

Common calcaneal
tendon

9

8

4

Extensor retinacula

7

5

4'

9'

6

Lateral

Left hindlimb.

1. Minor psoas m.
2. Iliopsoas m.
3. Sartorial m. (cut ends)
4. Tensor of fascia lata m.
5. Femoral quadriceps m.
      a. Straight femoral m.
      b. Medial vast m.
6. Pectineal m.
7. Popliteal m.
8. Long digital extensor m.
8'. Tendon of 8
9. Cranial tibial m.
9'. Tendon of 9
10. Third peroneal m.
11. Middle interosseous m.
      (suspensory ligament)

12. Deep digital flexor m.
      a. Medial head
      b. Superficial head
      c. Deep head
12'. Tendon of 12
13. Superficial digital flexor m.
13'. Tendon of 13
14. Gastrocnemius m.
      (medial head)
15. Gracile m. (cut ends)
16. Adductor m.
17. Semitendinous m.
18. Semimembranous m.
19. Internal obturator m.

The iliopsoas, tensor of the fascia lata, sartorial, pectineal and straight femoral muscles act to flex the hip joint.

The sartorial, gracile, pectineal and adductor muscles adduct the hindlimb (move it toward the midline).

The adductor and semimembranous muscles help to extend the hip joint.

Plate 34

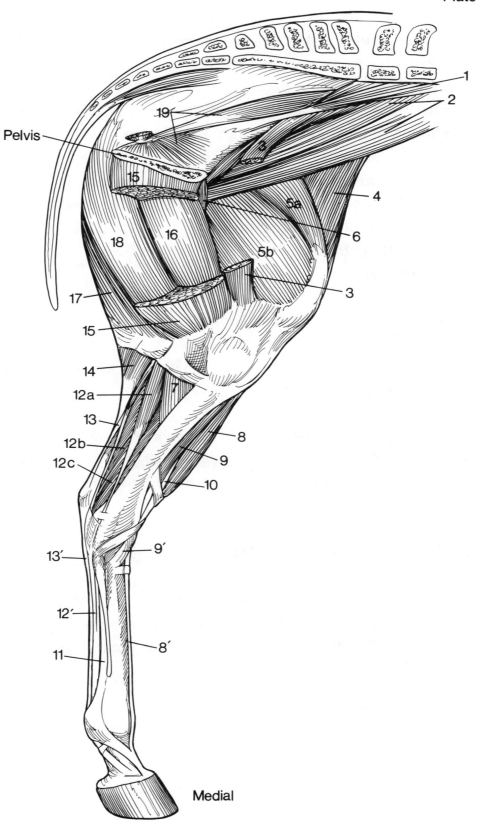

Pelvis

Medial

1
2
19
4
5a
6
5b
18
16
3
17
15
14
12a
7
13
12b
8
12c
9
10
13'
9'
12'
8'
11

Figure 1. Cranial view of right leg.
Figure 2. Caudal view of right leg. m.= muscle

   1. Lateral digital extensor m.

   2. Long digital extensor m.

   3. Third peroneal m. (Deep to long digital extensor. Color over the dashed lines.)

   3'. Tendons of insertion of the third peroneal m.

   4. Cranial tibial m.

   4'. Medial tendon of cranial tibial m. (cunean tendon)

   5. Medial head of gastrocnemius m.   (These two heads conceal the

   6. Lateral head of gastrocnemius m.   superficial digital flexor muscle belly.)

   7. Tendon of gastrocnemius m.

   8. Tendon of superficial digital flexor m.

   9. Deep digital flexor m. - three heads

  10 . Deep digital flexor tendon (Formed by conjoined tendons
                                    of the three heads.)

   11. Tarsal sheath - encloses tendon of caudal tibial and deep heads of deep digital
            flexor muscle.

The lateral tendon of insertion of the third peroneal muscle attaches to the fourth
tarsal bone and the calcaneus. The medial (cunean) tendon of the cranial tibial
muscle passes over a very large bursa on the way to its attachment on the first
tarsal bone.

Anular ligaments support and hold tendons in place.

Swelling of the hock caudally without lameness usually indicates inflammation of the
tarsal sheath around the deep digital flexor tendon as it passes over the
sustentaculum tali of the calcaneus. This condition is called thoroughpin.

Plate 35

Figure 1

Figure 2

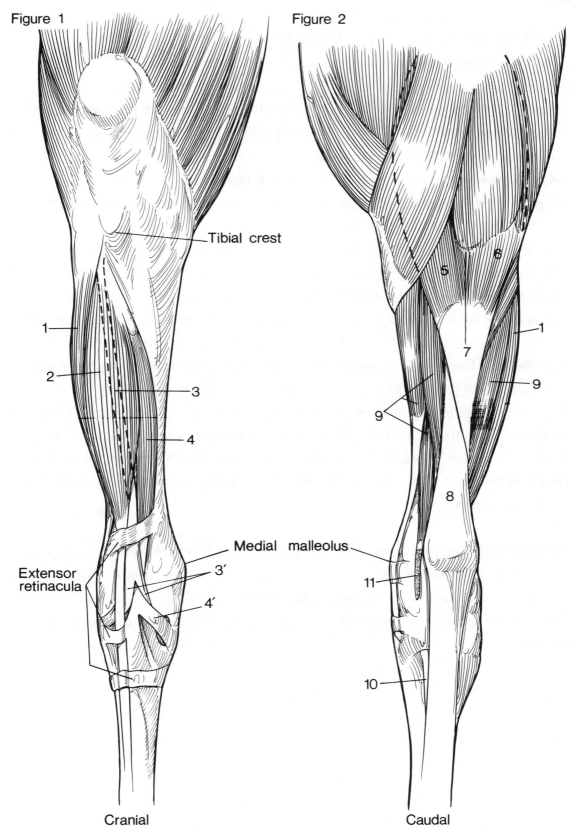

Tibial crest

Medial malleolus

Extensor
retinacula

Cranial

Caudal

Figure 1. Stay apparatus of left hindlimb.

Figure 2. Partly flexed, relaxed right hindlimb.

Figure 3. Dissection of reciprocal apparatus.

1. **Tensor of fascia lata m.**
2. **Femoral quadriceps m.**
3. **Patellar ligaments**
4. **Superficial digital flexor m.**
5. **Third peroneal m.**
   (deep to long digital extensor m.)
6. **Long digital extensor tendon**
7. **Subtarsal check ligament to 8**
8. **Deep digital flexor tendon**
9. **Suspensory ligament**
9'. **Extensor branch of 9**
10. **Distal sesamoidean ligaments**

While one hindlimb is partly flexed with the toe resting on the ground, the stay apparatus of the opposite hindlimb fixes its foot firmly on the ground. Contraction of the tensor of the fascia lata and the femoral quadriceps muscles pulls the patella, parapatellar cartilage and medial patellar ligament proximad to lock temporarily over the medial ridge of the femur's trochlea. The third peroneal muscle cranially and the superficial digital flexor muscle caudally act against one another to lock the hock joints. Only a small amount of muscular activity is needed to keep the stifle and hock joints locked. In this fixed position, overextension of the fetlock joint is prevented by the superficial and deep digital flexor tendons, the extensor branches of the suspensory ligament (middle interosseous m.) joining the long digital extensor tendon, and the three distal sesamoidean ligaments. Flexors of the stifle "unlock" the fixed position of the stay apparatus.

Reciprocal apparatus: When the stifle joints flex, the femur pulls on the third peroneal muscle, flexing the tarsocrural joint. When the stifle is extended, the femur pulls on the superficial digital flexor, extending the hock.

Flexion of the stifle without flexion of the hock indicates rupture of the third peroneal muscle.

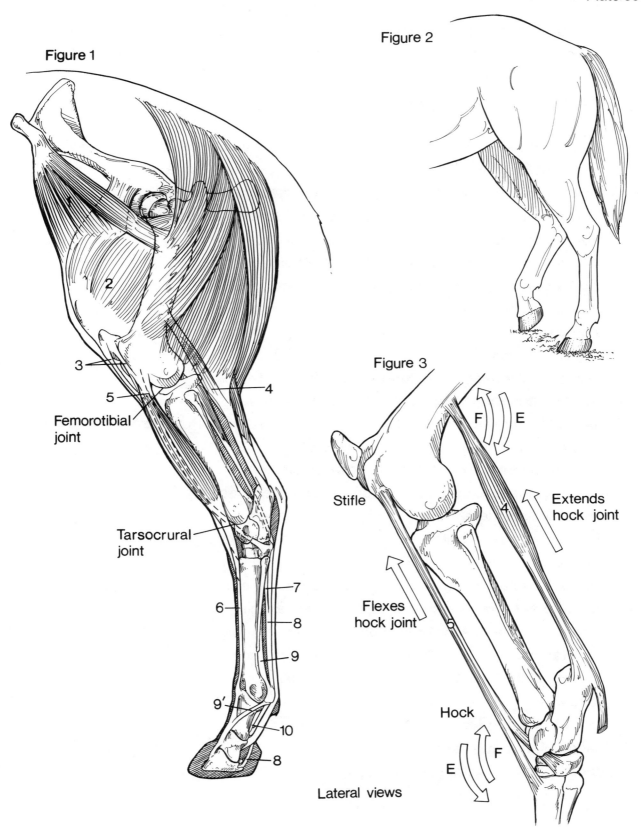

Plate 36

Figure 1

Figure 2

2

3

5

4

Femorotibial
joint

Tarsocrural
joint

6

7

8

9

9'

10

8

Figure 3

Stifle

F   E

Extends
hock joint

4

Flexes
hock joint

5

Hock

E   F

Lateral views

Hindlimb nerves arise from the **lumbosacral plexus,** a network formed by ventral branches of the fourth, fifth and sixth lumbar nerves and the first two sacral nerves. Trace the course of each nerve in a different color.

n.= nerve; nn.= nerves; m.= muscle;

Figure 1. Medial view of right hindlimb skeleton with the courses of the major nerves drawn roughly upon it.

Figure 2. Lateral view of left hindlimb showing courses of cutaneous nerves.

  1. Femoral n. - motor to sublumbar and femoral quadriceps mm.

  1a. Saphenous n. - motor to sartorial muscle; sensory to medial limb.

  2. Obturator n. - motor to adductor muscles of hip

  3. Caudal gluteal n. - motor to femoral biceps and semitendinous muscles.

  3a. Caudal cutaneous femoral n. - from 3 - sensory to skin

  4. Sciatic (ischiadic) n. - motor to femoral biceps, semitendinous and semimembranous muscles

  5. Common peroneal n. - motor branch to femoral biceps m.

  5a. Lateral cutaneous sural n. - from 5 - sensory to skin

  6. Superficial peroneal n. - motor to lateral digital extensor m.; sensory to skin of leg, hock and metatarsus

  7. Deep peroneal n. - motor to long digital extensor m.

  8. Lateral dorsal metatarsal n. ⎤ sensory to fetlock, pastern

  9. Medial dorsal metatarsal n. ⎦ and <u>laminar</u> <u>corium</u>

  10. Tibial n. - motor to digital flexors, popliteal and gastrocnemius muscles; sensory to hock joint

  10a. Caudal cutaneous sural n. - from 10 - sensory to skin

  11. Lateral plantar n. - sensory to lateral aspect of digit

  11a. Deep branch of 11 - motor to interosseous m.; divides into medial and lateral plantar metatarsal nn. deep to interosseous m., sensory to plantar pouch of fetlock joint. (Deep branch from the forelimb's lateral palmar n. has same pattern.)

  12. Communicating branch - small, may be absent

  13. Medial plantar n. - sensory to medial aspect of digit

  14. Medial plantar digital n. - continuation of 13

  15. Dorsal branch of 14

Plate 37

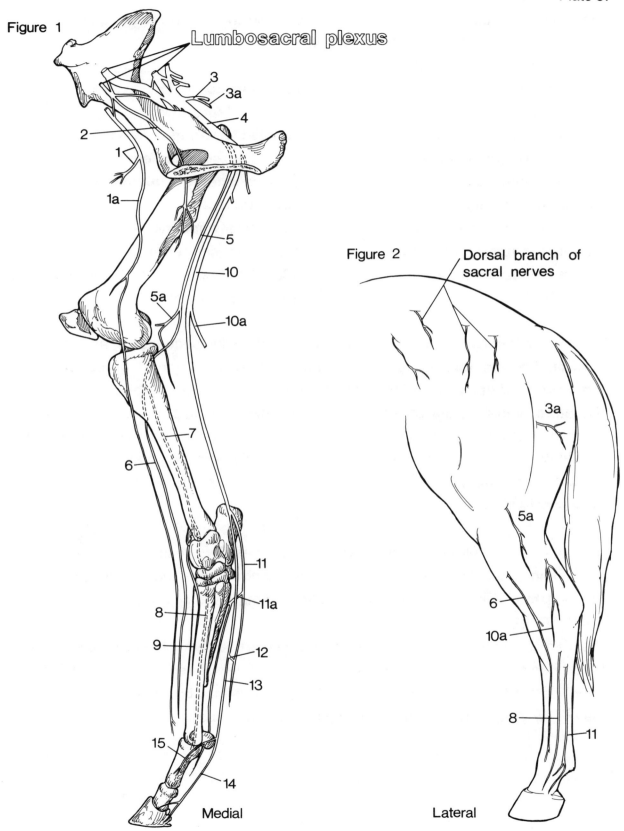

Figure 1

Lumbosacral plexus

3
3a
4
2
1
1a
5
10
5a
10a
7
6
11
11a
8
9
12
13
15
14

Medial

Figure 2

Dorsal branch of
sacral nerves

3a

5a

6

10a

8

11

Lateral

Color the courses of the vessels indicated. Dashed lines trace vessels on the opposite side of the limb. a.= artery; v.= vein

Major Arteries	Major Veins
1. Obturator a.	**10. Obturator v.**
2. Deep femoral a.	**11. Deep femoral v.**
3. Med. circumflex femoral a.	**12. Med. circumflex femoral v.**
4. Lat. circumflex femoral a.	**13. Lat. circumflex femoral v.**
5. Descending genicular a.	**14. Descending genicular v.**
6. Caudal femoral a.	**15. Caudal femoral v.**
7. Proximal perforating branch	**16. Lateral saphenous v.**
8. Medial & lateral plantar aa.	**17. Medial saphenous v.**
9. Med. and lat. plantar metatarsal aa.	**18. Caudal branch 17**
	19. Medial plantar v.

Blood to the hindfoot flows primarily through the following sequence of arteries: **external iliac - femoral - popliteal - cranial tibial - dorsal pedal - lateral dorsal metatarsal - distal perforating branch - medial and lateral digital aa.**
The lateral dorsal metatarsal artery can be palpated and the pulse felt as it runs in the groove formed by the lateral small and large metatarsal bones. The artery then passes between the two bones to become the distal perforating branch that receives plantar and plantar metatarsal arteries before dividing into the medial and lateral digital arteries.

Most veins are satellites (companions) of the arteries. Two veins accompany the cranial and caudal tibial arteries. The cranial branch of the medial saphenous vein and the lateral saphenous vein are exceptions in that each courses alone under the skin.
The cranial branch of the medial saphenous vein is usually visible as it runs under the skin across the dorsal aspect of the hock. If the vein is very distended (full of blood) here, the swelling is termed blood spavin. This may be confused with bog spavin, swelling of the inflamed dorsal pouch of the tarsocrural joint.

Plate 38

Arteries

Veins

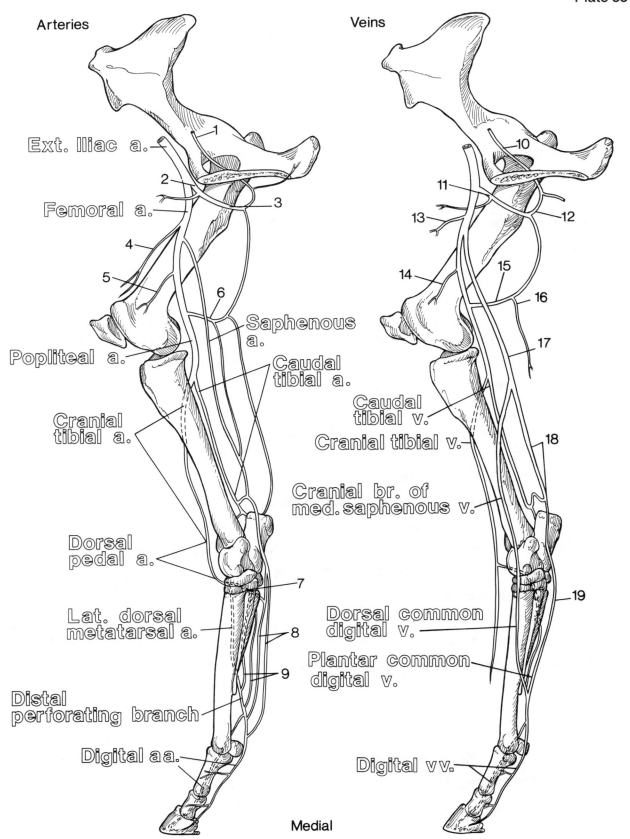

Ext. Iliac a. — 1

Femoral a. — 2, 3

4

5

6 — Saphenous a.

Popliteal a. — Caudal tibial a.

Cranial tibial a.

Dorsal pedal a. — 7

Lat. dorsal metatarsal a. — 8

9

Distal perforating branch

Digital aa.

10

11, 12

13

14, 15, 16

17

Caudal tibial v.

Cranial tibial v.

18

Cranial br. of med. saphenous v.

19

Dorsal common digital v.

Plantar common digital v.

Digital vv.

Medial

Color the dashed lines from P (proximal) to D (distal). Arrows indicate **offset knees.**

A line dropped from the point of the shoulder (middle of the shoulder joint) bisects a **normal forelimb.**

Base-narrow (B-n) conformation causes the lateral wall to land first, bear most of the weight and wear faster. The medial wall should be trimmed to level the foot.

In base-wide (B-w) conformation more weight falls on the medial side (inside) of the foot where it lands first, causing the medial hoof wall to wear faster. The lateral (outside) wall should be trimmed to level the foot.

Offset knees (bench knees) place greater strain on the medial small metacarpal (splint) bone, often leading to "splints" (inflammation of the interosseous ligament and the splint bone).

Undesirable gaits resulting from abnormal conformations:

Winging - **Toe-out conformation** usually causes the forefoot to break over the medial side of the toe and arc to the inside.

Paddling - **Toe-in conformation** usually results in the forefoot swinging to the outside as it leaves the ground.

Plaiting - In **base-narrow, toe-out conformation** one forefoot travels inward to land cranial to the other forefoot, causing more locomotion problems than other abnormal conformations.

In a lateral view of a **normal forelimb,** a line dropped from the tuber of the scapular spine bisects the limb as far as the fetlock and continues distad just caudal to the heel.

Calf knees (palmar deviation of the carpal joints) puts great strain of the ligaments associated with the palmar aspect of the carpus and increases compression on the dorsal aspect of the carpal bones. Chip fractures of the third, intermediate and radial carpal bones and the distal end of the radius may occur.

Plate 39

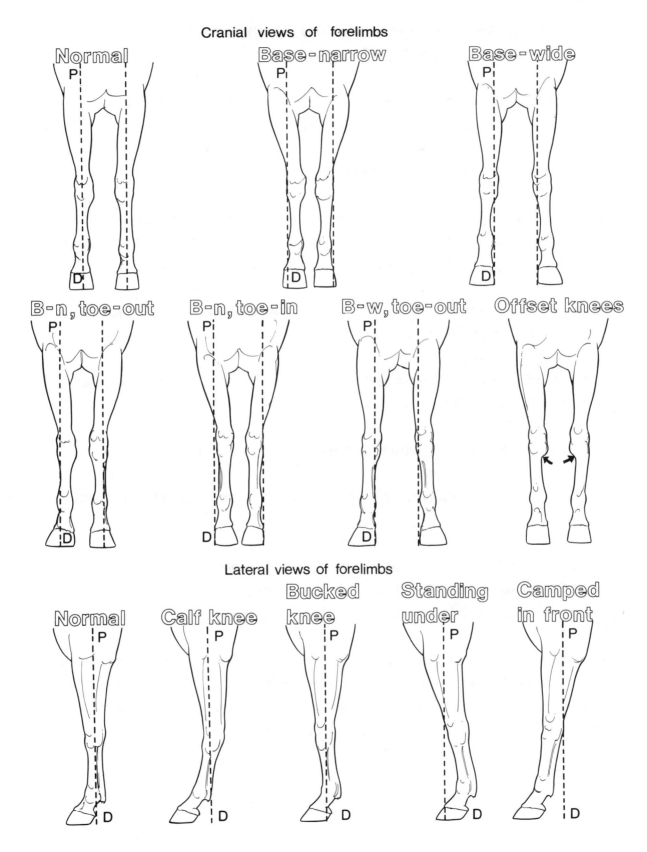

Color the dashed lines from P (proximal) to D (distal). Caudally, a line dropped from the point of the ischiadic tuber ("pin bone") bisects a **normal hindlimb.**

Base-narrow behind conformation places heavy stress on the structures on the lateral side of the hindlimb. Even if the forelimbs are normal, this abnormal hindlimb conformation can cause interference between forelimbs and hindlimbs. "<u>Bowlegs</u>" are frequently associated with this conformation.

In **cow-hocked** conformation, hindlimbs are base-narrow to the hocks and base-wide from the hocks to the feet. Excessive strain is placed upon the medial side of the hock, possibly contributing to the development of bone spavin.

In a lateral view of a **normal hindlimb,** a line dropped from the ischiadic tuber extends along the caudal surface of the metatarsus.

In both **standing under behind** and **sickle hock,** the metatarsus and digit are aligned well forward of the normal position.

Sickle hocks place a heavy strain on the long plantar ligament that attaches to the calcaneus, fourth tarsal bone and fourth metatarsal bone of each hock. The constant strain can cause <u>curb</u>, a painful inflammation and thickening of the long plantar ligament.

Too straight behind conformation may be prone to developing <u>bog spavin</u> and <u>upward</u> <u>fixation</u> <u>of the</u> <u>patella</u>, causing the patella to ride up and lock over the medial ridge of the trochlea of the femur.

Short upright pasterns may lead to injuries of the fetlock joint, <u>ringbone</u> (inflammation and excess bone formation) of the pastern joint, and <u>navicular disease</u>. These problems occur more commonly in the fetlock joint, pastern joint and coffin joint of the forelimb.

Plate 40

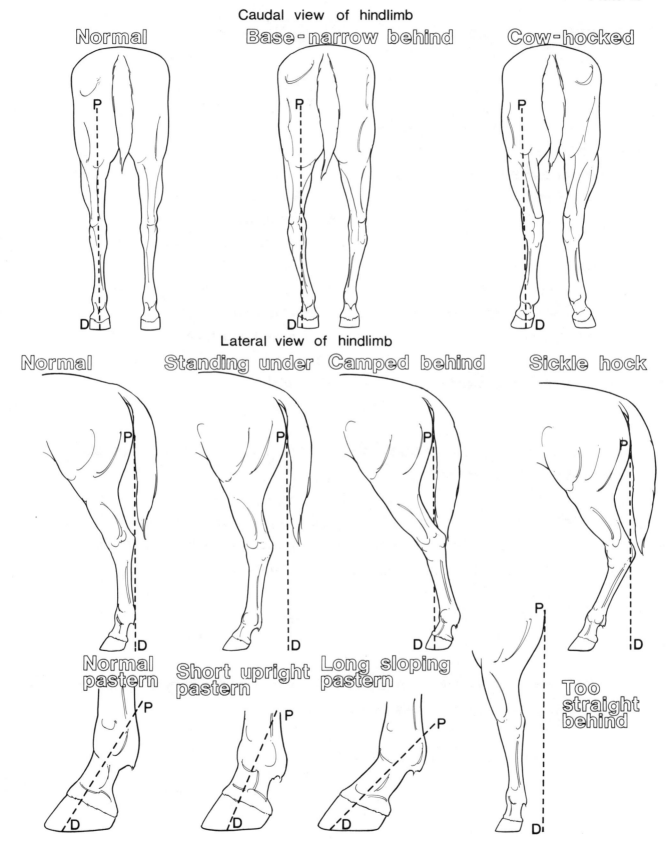

Caudal view of hindlimb

Normal   Base-narrow behind   Cow-hocked

Lateral view of hindlimb

Normal   Standing under   Camped behind   Sickle hock

Normal pastern   Short upright pastern   Long sloping pastern

Too straight behind

THE SKULL

Figure 1. Left lateral view of skull.

Figure 2. Ventral view of skull. Mandible removed.

Identify the parts of bones listed below:

1. Nuchal crest   of   **10. Zygomatic arch**

2. Occipital condyle   occipital   **11. Zygomatic process** of frontal bone

3. Jugular process bone bone   **12. Supraorbital foramen**

                                          13. Facial crest

4. Temporomandibular joint   **14. Infraorbital foramen**

5. Coronoid process   **15. Foramen magnum (great f.)**

6. Mandibular foramen   **16. Foramen lacerum (jagged f.)**

       (on medial side of ramus)   **17. Orbital fissure**

7. Mental foramen   **18. Caudal alar foramen**

8. Notch for facial vessels   **19. Hamulus of pterygoid bone**

9. External acoustic meatus   **20. Incisive canal**

Since sutures are fibrous joints that ossify with age, junctions between most bones of the skull become indistinct.

Notice that the upper **canine tooth (C), premolars (P1- P4)** and **molars (M1- M3)** are in alveoli (sockets) in each **maxilla.** The upper **incisor teeth (I1- I3)** are in the **incisive bones.** All of the lower teeth are in the **mandible.**

The spinal cord passes through the **foramen magnum** (great f.). Blood vessels and nerves pass through the many foramina (plural of foramen) in the skull.

In life, the large, irregular **foramen lacerum** (jagged f.) is filled in by a membrane that admits the passage of vessels and nerves.

The inner end of the **external acoustic meatus** is covered by the eardrum.

Plate 41

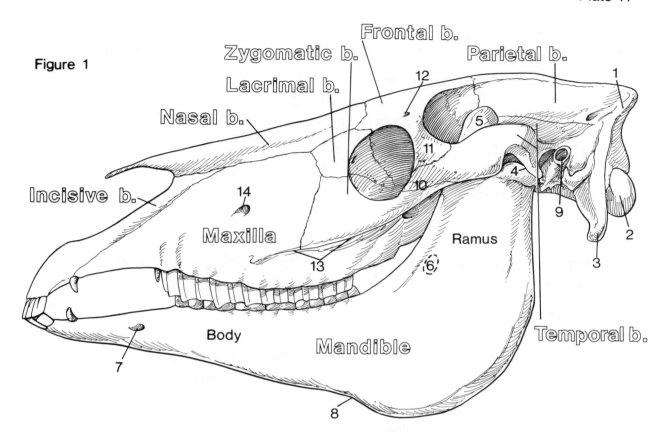

Figure 1

Frontal b.

Zygomatic b.

Parietal b.

Lacrimal b.

Nasal b.

Incisive b.

14

Maxilla

Body

Ramus

Mandible

Temporal b.

12

11

10

5

4

1

9

2

3

6

13

7

8

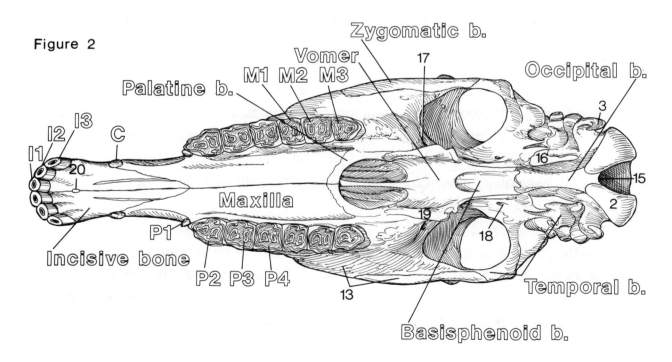

Figure 2

Zygomatic b.

Vomer

Palatine b.

M1 M2 M3

17

Occipital b.

I3

I2

C

I1

20

Maxilla

Incisive bone

P1

P2 P3 P4

13

Basisphenoid b.

19

18

16

3

15

2

Temporal b.

Figure 1. Midsagittal section of skull. Cartilaginous nasal septum (partition) removed.

Figure 2. Lateral view of skull with paranasal sinuses exposed. Hyoid apparatus pulled away from its attachments to skull.

Identify the bones, cavities and parts of bones listed below:

1. **Dorsal nasal meatus (passageway)**
2. **Dorsal nasal concha**
3. **Middle nasal meatus**
4. **Ventral nasal concha**
5. **Ventral nasal meatus**
6. **Ethmoturbinates**
7. **Nasal bone**
8. **Incisive bone**
9. **Maxilla**
10. **Vomer**
11. **Palatine bone**
12. **Pterygoid bone**
13. **Basisphenoid bone**
14. **Occipital bone**
15. **Petrous part of temporal bone**
16. **Infraorbital canal**
17. **Lingual process of basihyoid bone**
18. **Ceratohyoid bones**
19. **Thyrohyoid bones**
20. **Stylohyoid bones**

The nasal septum divides the **nasal cavity** into halves.

A bony and membranous septum divides the **maxillary sinus** into rostral and caudal compartments.

The **infraorbital canal** traverses the maxillary sinus, extending from the maxillary foramen (in the orbit) to the infraorbital foramen. The canal contains the infraorbital nerve - the sensory supply to the upper teeth, maxillary sinus, nasal region and lips.

The maxillary sinus communicates with the **nasal cavity** through an opening into the **middle nasal meatus.**

The **stylohyoids** attach to the petrous (stonelike) part of each temporal bone; the **thyrohyoids** attach to the larynx; and the **lingual process of the basihyoid** is embedded in the root of the tongue. The complex of hyoid bones constitutes the **hyoid apparatus** that supports the guttural pouches, pharynx, larynx and root of the tongue.

Plate 42

Figure 1

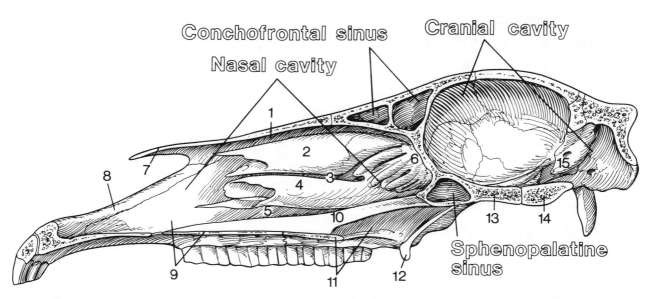

Conchofrontal sinus   Cranial cavity

Nasal cavity

Sphenopalatine sinus

Figure 2

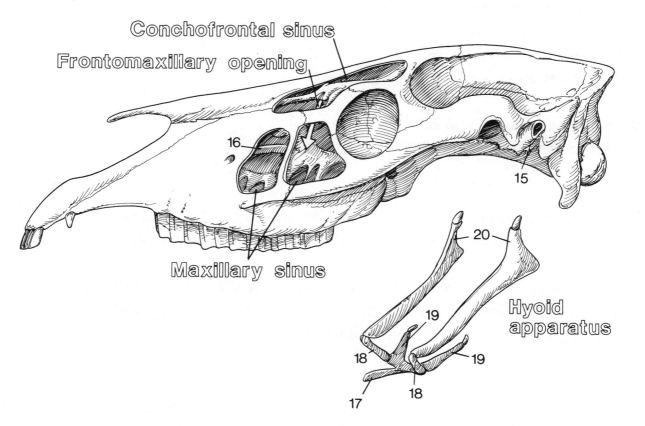

Conchofrontal sinus

Frontomaxillary opening

Maxillary sinus

Hyoid apparatus

Superficial dissection of right side of head.

1. **Parotidoauricular muscle**
2. **Parotid salivary gland**
3. **Great auricular nerve**
4. **Caudal auricular muscles**
5. **Scutiform cartilage**
6. **Rostral auricular muscles**
7. **Transverse facial artery, vein and nerve**
8. **Eyelids**
9. **Angular artery and vein of the eye**
10. **Nasolabial levator muscle**
11. **Superior labial levator muscle**
12. **Canine muscle**
13. **Nostril**
14. **Oral orbicular muscle**
15. **Inferior labial depressor muscle**
16. **Buccinator muscle**
17. **Zygomatic muscle**
18. **Facial cutaneous muscle**
19. **Masseter muscle**
20. **Facial nerve**
21. **Masseteric artery and vein**
22. **Auricular (conchal) cartilage**
23. **External jugular vein**

Right and left **superior labial levator muscles** join in a <u>common</u> <u>tendon</u> that spreads out in the upper lip. Contraction of these muscles raises the upper lip.

The superficially located **facial nerve** can be injured by a blow to overlying halter parts, resulting in paralysis of facial muscles on that side. The muzzle is then pulled to the opposite side by the functioning muscles there.

Plate 43

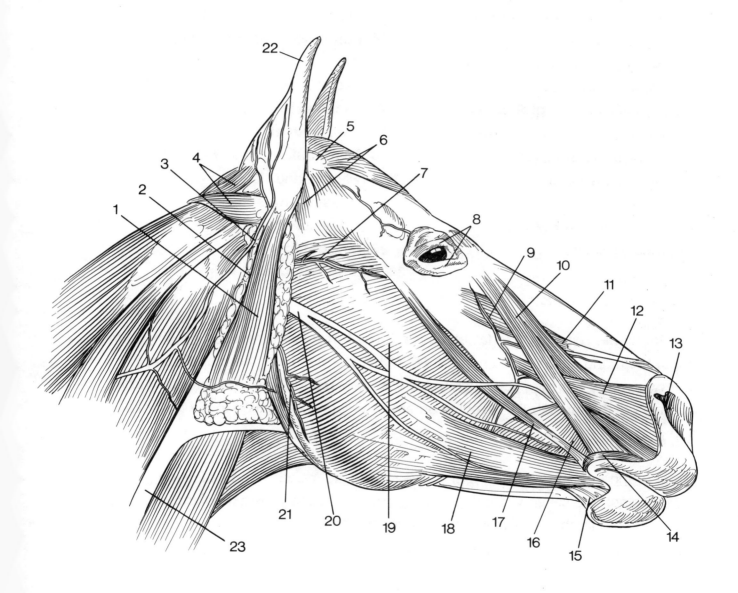

Deeper dissection of right side of head. Superficial muscles removed. a.= artery; v.= vein; n.= nerve.

1. **Maxillary vein**
2. **Mandibular salivary gland**
3. **Occipitomandibular muscle**
4. **Facial nerve** (cut)
5. **Caudal auricular a.v.n.**
6. **Rostral auricular a.v.n.**
7. **Superficial temporal artery**
8. **Anastomotic** (joining) **branch with transverse facial vein**
9. **Deep facial vein**
10. **Buccal vein**
11. **Buccal salivary gland**
12. **Infraorbital nerve**
13. **Dorsal nasal artery and vein**
14. **Lateral nasal a. and v.**
15. **Mental nerve**
16. **Penetration of cheek by parotid duct**
17. **Facial artery**
18. **Facial vein**
19. **Parotid duct**
20. **Mandibular alveolar n.** (within mandible)
21. **Masseter muscle** (partly cut away)
22. **Linguofacial vein**
23. **External jugular vein**

The **facial nerve** is <u>motor</u> to facial muscles. The **infraorbital nerve** is <u>sensory</u> to the upper teeth and gums, face and muzzle. Within the mandible, the **mandibular alveolar nerve** <u>supplies</u> <u>sensation</u> to the lower teeth and gums. The **mental nerve,** a branch of the mandibular alveolar, emerges to <u>supply</u> <u>sensation</u> to the lower lip and chin.

<u>Motor</u> <u>branches</u> of the **mandibular nerve** supply the muscles of mastication (chewing muscles) and salivary glands; <u>sensory</u> <u>branches</u> supply the skin of the cheek and ear, lining of the cheek and the tongue (except taste).

Plate 44

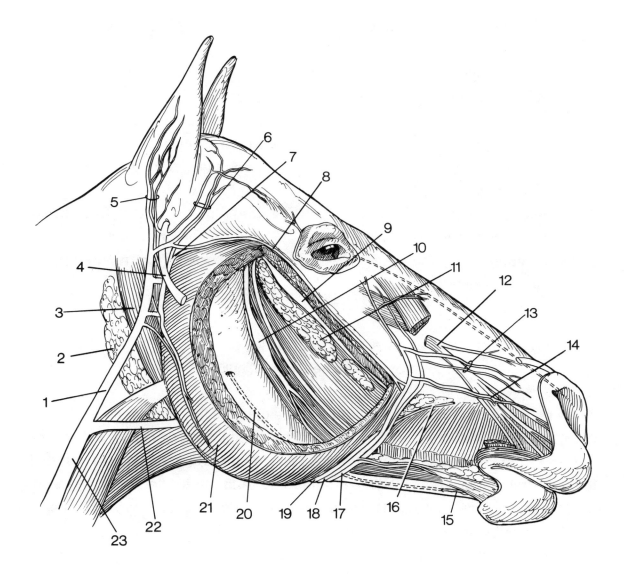

Figure 1. Horse's head showing course of nasolacrimal duct.
Figure 2. External parts of left eye. Eyelids slightly everted to show tarsal (oil) glands and lacrimal puncta.
Figure 3. Left nostril. Medial wing and its supporting <u>alar</u> <u>cartilage</u> elevated.

Do not color the cornea and lens, since they are transparent.

1. **Position of lacrimal gland** (deep to zygomatic process)
2. **Iris**
3. **Iridic granules** (pigmented)
4. **Sclera ("white of eye")**
5. **Cornea** (transparent)
6. **Openings of tarsal glands**
7. **Third eyelid**
8. **Lacrimal puncta**
9. **Lacrimal canals**
10. **Lacrimal sac**
11. **Nasolacrimal duct**
12. **Lacrimal caruncle**
13. **Lens** (seen through <u>pupil</u>, opening in the iris)
14. **Nasal diverticulum (false nostril)**
15. **Lateral wing of nostril**
16. **Nasal opening of nasolacrimal duct**
17. **Medial wing of nostril**

Color the arrows: Small arrow enters nasal cavity.
                  Large arrow enters nasal diverticulum.

Tears secreted by the **lacrimal gland** and the <u>gland</u> <u>of</u> <u>the</u> <u>third</u> <u>eyelid</u> (not seen here) wash over the surface of the eye, collecting at the medial <u>canthus</u> (junction of the lids). Tears then flow through the two **lacrimal puncta** and **lacrimal canals** into the **lacrimal sac** and continue into the **nasolacrimal duct.** After traversing a bony canal in the lacrimal bone and maxilla, the nasolacrimal duct is covered by cartilage and then continues under the mucous membrane of the nasal cavity to its **nasal opening** in the floor of the nostril near the skin's junction with the mucous membrane.

A blocked nasolacrimal duct causes overflow of tears (<u>epiphora</u>). A small tube pushed through the lower lacrimal punctum and into the duct can be used to locate and correct an obstruction.

Plate 45

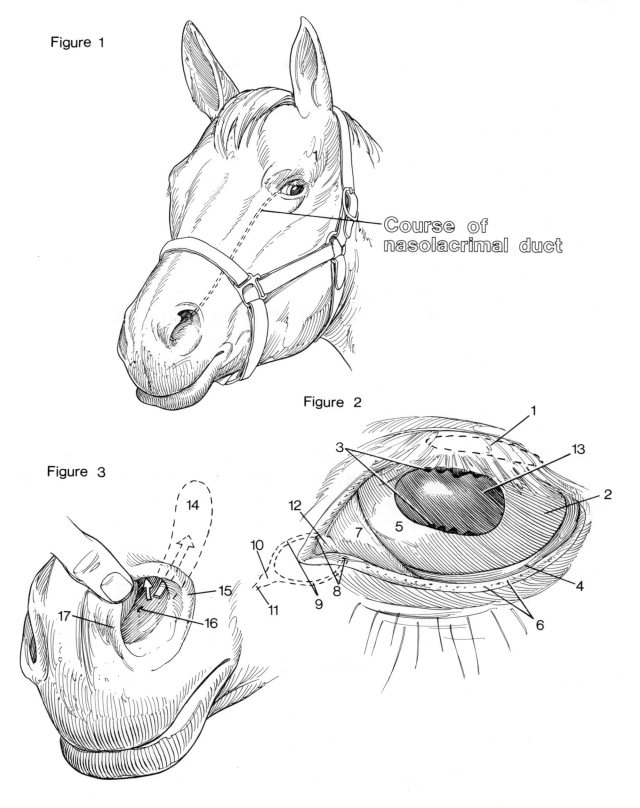

Figure 1

Course of nasolacrimal duct

Figure 2

Figure 3

Figure 1. Caudal part of sagittal section of head.
Arrow indicates **pharyngeal opening of auditory tube** under a ridge of cartilage.

Figure 2. Ventral view of guttural pouches. Lower jaw, tongue, larynx, and most of the pharynx removed.

a.= artery; n.= nerve; lnn.= lymph nodes

1. **Right guttural pouch**
   (ventral wall removed)
2. **Left guttural pouch**
3. **Med. retropharyngeal lnn.**
4. **Cranial laryngeal n.**
5. **Vagosympathetic nerve trunk**
6. **Ventral straight muscles of head**
7. **Common carotid a.**
8. **Internal carotid a.**
   (dashed lines against dorsal wall
   of medial compartment)
9. **Lateral compartment of guttural pouch**
10. **External carotid a.**
11. **Hypoglossal n.**
12. **Opening of auditory tube into guttural pouch**
13. **Glossopharyngeal n.**
14. **Lingual a.**
15. **Stylohyoid bone**

A **guttural pouch** is a large, caudoventral outpocketing (diverticulum) of the **auditory tube,** a tube extending from the pharynx to the middle ear in the temporal bone and serving to equalize pressure on the inside of the eardrum. Guttural pouches occur only in equids - horses, donkeys, zebras. Caudoventrally the guttural pouch is folded around the styohyoid bone, forming communicating medial and lateral compartments.

Lymph nodes, blood vessels and nerves lying against a guttural pouch can be damaged by fungal or bacterial infections spreading from the pouch. Erosion of an arterial wall with hemorrhage into the guttural pouch can be fatal. Discharges of pus or blood from a nostril when the horse lowers its head may indicate such a condition. Abnormal filling of a guttural pouch with air (tympany) can occur in a foal. A distended guttural pouch causes swelling in the parotid region.

Notice the position of the soft palate as it has moved from the breathing position at the base of the epiglottis toward the caudal wall of the pharynx.

Plate 46

Figure 1

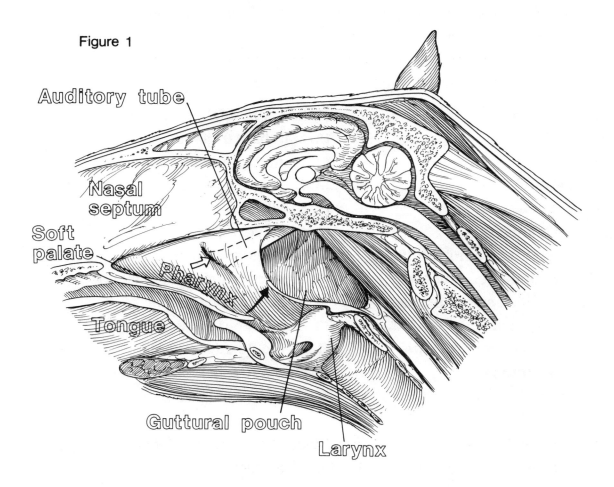

Auditory tube

Nasal septum

Soft palate

Pharynx

Tongue

Guttural pouch

Larynx

Figure 2

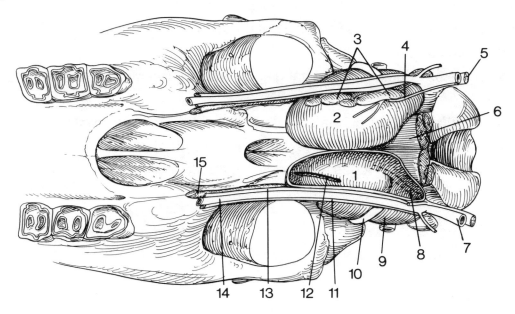

Figure 1. Ventral view of head. Superficial dissection. Facial cutaneous muscle
         removed on left side.
Figure 2. Deeper dissection with mandible split at symphysis and halves displaced
         laterad. Most of mylohyoid muscles removed.

1. Parotid gland	**11. Inferior labial depressor m.**
2. Parotid duct	**12. Mandibular gland**
3. Facial vein	**13. Mandibular duct**
4. Facial artery	**14. Sublingual gland**
5. Left ramus of mandible	**15. Sublingual caruncle**
6. Body of mandible	**16. Basihyoid bone**
7. Sternohyoid and omohyoid mm.	**17. Hypoglossal n.** - motor to tongue
8. R. facial cutaneous muscle	**18. Lingual n.** - sensory to tongue
(removed on left side to expose	**19. Styloglossus muscle**
masseter muscle)	**20. Geniohyoid muscle**
9. R. mandibular lymphocenter	**21. Genioglossus muscle**
10. Mylohyoid muscle	**22. Oral mucous membrane**
	23. Apex (tip) **of tongue**

The palpable lymph nodes of the two **mandibular lymphocenters** enlarge and may
abscess in a case of <u>strangles</u> (viral + streptococcal infection).

Saliva enters the oral cavity at the following locations:
1. The **parotid duct** opens on a papilla of mucous membrane opposite the third
   upper cheek tooth (P4).
2. Numerous small ducts from <u>buccal glands</u> open on the mucous membrane of the
   cheek.
3. Each **mandibular duct** opens on a flattened **sublingual caruncle.**
4. Many short, twisted ducts from each **sublingual gland** open on small papillae on
   a sublingual fold of mucous membrane on the floor of the oral cavity.

Plate 47

Figure 1

Figure 2

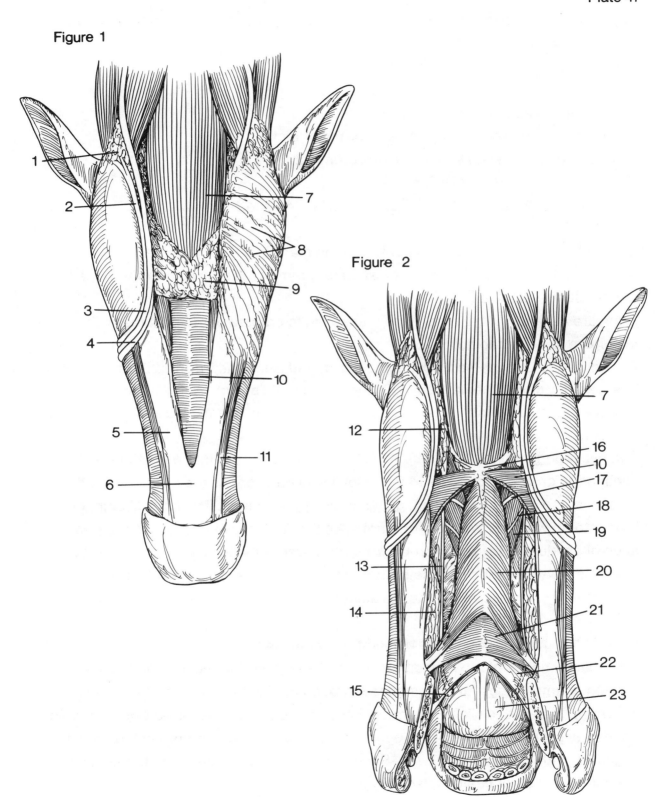

Figure 1. Sagittal section (right) and occlusal surfaces (left) of a permanent lower
        first incisor tooth.
Figure 2. Complete permanent dentition.

 Abbreviations and dental formulae:
I = incisor, C = canine, P = premolar, M = molar teeth
Di = deciduous incisor, Dp = deciduous premolar (No Dc or Dm's)
Deciduous teeth: 2(Di3/3 Dp3/3) = 24
Permanent teeth: 2(I3/3 C1/1 P 3 or 4/3 M3/3) = 40 or 42

Canine teeth are absent or rudimentary in the mare.
A **wolf tooth** is a small, inconstant first upper premolar. It may interfere with the bit
and is usually extracted.
Caps are deciduous teeth that remain attached to erupted permanent teeth. They
may have to be extracted.
A yellowish layer of cement covers the crown and fills in the **infundibulum** of central
enamel. The **cup** is the dark cavity in the early infundibulum. With time, cement
wears away over the crown, exposing the white enamel. Cement is maintained over
the root.
The hypsodont teeth of the horse have long reserve crowns that permit the teeth to
continue to grow out for 12 to 14 years following eruption. As they wear down, the
shapes of the occlusal (meeting, grinding) surfaces change. The infundibulum of an
incisor tooth wears down to an **enamel spot** that is soon worn away. The appear-
ance of an elongated, yellowish-brown **dental star** to the lip side of the infundibulum
indicates wear into the tip of the **pulp cavity** that has been filled in with **secondary
dentin.** At first elongated, the dental star changes to circular as the tooth wears
down.
Wear in the upper incisors lags behind that of the lowers.
The enamel ridges of the infundibula of the cheek teeth (premolars and molars)
provide enamel ridges for grinding feed through the lateral motion of the narrower
lower jaw. Due to this slightly narrower lower jaw, sharp ridges called **points** develop
on the buccal (cheek) side of the upper cheek teeth (molars and premolars) and the
lingual (tongue) side of the lowers. Sharp points can cut the cheek or tongue and
have to be cut off or floated (filed down).

Plate 48

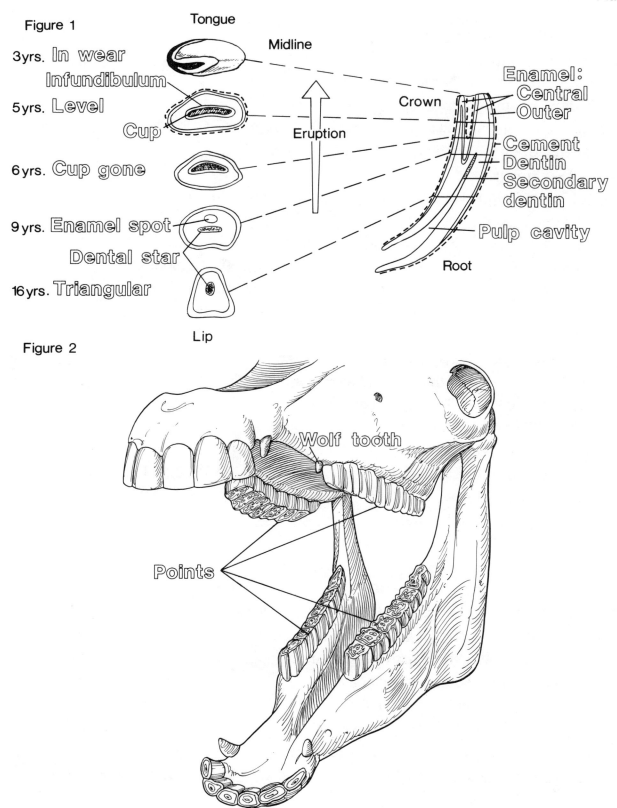

Figure 1

Tongue

Midline

3yrs. In wear

Infundibulum

5yrs. Level

Cup

Eruption

Crown

6yrs. Cup gone

9yrs. Enamel spot

Dental star

16yrs. Triangular

Lip

Enamel:
Central
Outer

Cement
Dentin
Secondary
dentin

Pulp cavity

Root

Figure 2

Wolf tooth

Points

Identify the teeth on the drawings.

<u>Average</u> <u>Eruption</u> <u>Times</u>:

<u>Deciduous</u> <u>Teeth</u>. Smaller. Neck between crown and root.

Cement worn away over crown, exposing white enamel.

Di1(central) - Birth or first week	Dp2	⎰	Birth
Di2 (intermediate) - 4 to 6 weeks	Dp3	⎱	or
Di3 (lateral) - 6 to 9 months	Dp4		first 2 weeks

<u>Permanent</u> <u>Teeth</u>. Larger. No neck. Newly erupted crown covered with yellowish cement. <u>In</u> <u>wear</u> <u>6</u> <u>months</u> <u>after</u> <u>eruption</u>.

I1 - 2 1/2 years	P1 (wolf tooth) - 5 to 6 months	
I2 - 3 1/2 years	P2 - 21/2 years	M1 - 9 - 12 months
I3 - 4 1/2 years	P3 - 3 years	M2 - 2 1/2 years
C - 4 1/2 to 5 years	P4 - 4 years	M3 - 3 1/2 to 4 years

<u>Progressive</u> <u>appearance</u> <u>of</u> <u>incisor</u> <u>teeth</u>:

Changes in lower incisors unless otherwise indicated.

See Plate 48 for changes on the occlusal surfaces.

1 year - Di1 & Di2 in wear; Di3's not in contact.

2 years - Di1& Di2 level; Di3 in wear.

21/2 years - I1s erupt; in wear at 3.

31/2 years - I2s erupt; in wear at 4.   RELIABLE TO TELL AGE

41/2 years - I3s erupt; in wear at 5.

5 years - Cs erupted; I1and I2 level;

     <u>full</u> <u>mouth</u>.

6 years - I1 cup gone

7 years - I2 cup gone; hook on upper I3.

8 years - I3 cup gone; dental star on I1.   VERY UNRELIABLE TO TELL AGE

9 years - I1 round; dental star on I2.

10 years - I2 round; **Galvayne's groove** appears on upper I3.

13 years - Small enamel spots on incisors

15 years - I1 triangular; dental stars round.

17 years - I2 triangular; enamel spots gone.

20 years - **Galvayne's groove** to occlusal surface.

The <u>lateral</u> <u>profile</u> <u>angle</u> <u>of</u> <u>incisors</u> becomes <u>more</u> <u>acute</u> <u>with</u> <u>age</u>. Notice changes in the profile from 7 to 20 years.

Plate 49

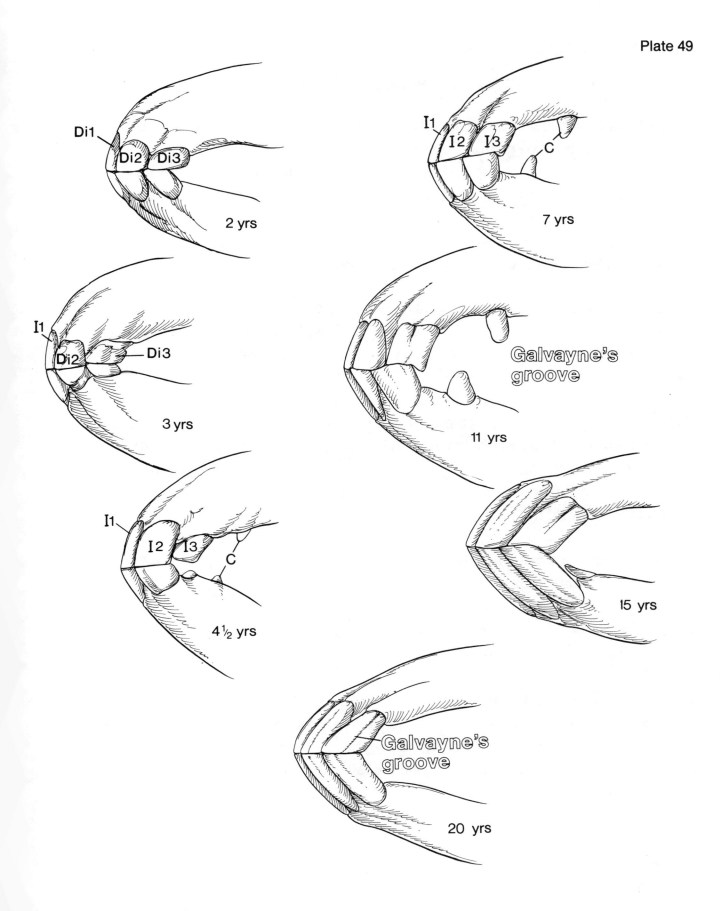

Di1
Di2 Di3
2 yrs

I1
I2 I3
C
7 yrs

I1
Di2 Di3
3 yrs

Galvayne's groove
11 yrs

I1
I2 I3
C
4½ yrs

15 yrs

Galvayne's groove
20 yrs

ORAL CAVITY, PHARYNX AND ESOPHAGUS

Figure 1. Right lateral view of a sagittal section of the head. **G.p.s. = Septum be-
        tween the two guttural pouches**
Figure 2. Dorsal view of tongue and dissected pharynx. The dorsal wall of the **na-
        sopharynx** is cut on the midline and each half pulled laterad. In a similar
        manner, the **soft palate** is cut and displaced. The free edge of the soft
        palate is continuous on each side with a **palatopharyngeal arch.** These
        arches unite over the entrance to the esophagus.

The **pharynx** is a musculomembranous chamber common to both the digestive and
respiratory tracts. Its three parts are: oropharynx, nasopharynx and laryngopharynx.
During breathing - the free edge of the soft palate is usually under the **epiglottis** and
the laryngeal entrance is open.
During swallowing - Mylohyoid and hyoglossus muscles raise the tongue, pressing
feed or water against the **hard palate.** The root of the tongue is pulled caudad, the
laryngeal entrance is narrowed, the epiglottis is pulled over the entrance, and the
long soft palate is elevated to the caudal wall of the pharynx. Increased pressure in
the pharynx forces feed or water into the **esophagus** where automatic contractions
carry material toward the stomach.

A variety of diseases can cause dorsal displacement of the soft palate, preventing its
return to the normal breathing position.

Vallate, foliate and fungiform papillae contain taste buds.
Filiform papillae are longer on the root of the tongue.

The esophagus (not seen here) follows a course at first dorsal and then down the
left face of the trachea, then dorsally on the trachea through the mediastinum (space
between the lungs) and finally through the esophageal hiatus (passage) in the diaphragm and to the stomach. Its position in the left side of the neck may be seen
during swallowing.

Plate 50

Figure 1

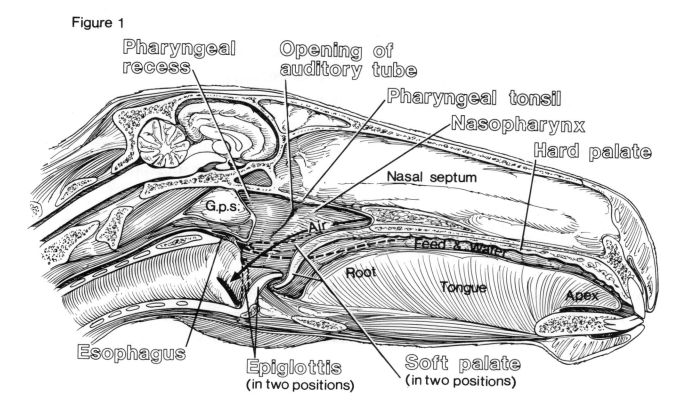

Pharyngeal recess — Opening of auditory tube — Pharyngeal tonsil — Nasopharynx — Hard palate — Nasal septum — G.p.s. — Air — Feed & water — Root — Tongue — Apex — Esophagus — Epiglottis (in two positions) — Soft palate (in two positions)

Figure 2

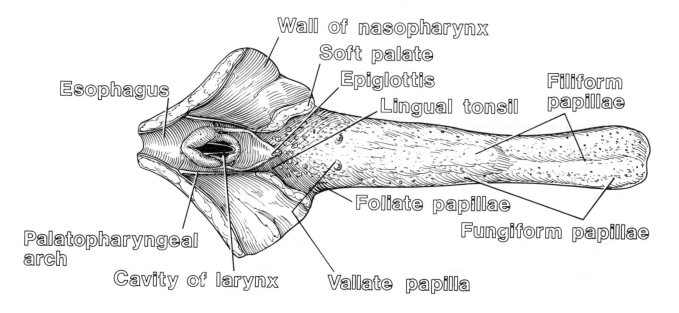

Esophagus — Wall of nasopharynx — Soft palate — Epiglottis — Lingual tonsil — Filiform papillae — Palatopharyngeal arch — Cavity of larynx — Foliate papillae — Vallate papilla — Fungiform papillae

Figure 1. Schematic drawing of the horse's stomach and small intestine viewed from
   the right.

1. **Esophagus**
2. **Cecal sac**
3. **Greater curvature**
4. **Lesser curvature**
5. **Pyloric antrum**

6. **Cranial part** ⎤
7. **Descending part** ⎟ **of**
8. **Ascending part** ⎦ **duodenum**

9. **Jejunum** ⎤ **Mesenteric part of**
10. **Ileum** ⎦ **small intestine**

Figure 2. The inside of the stomach and cranial part of the duodenum. Regions of
   the mucous membrane.

The relatively small stomach of the horse varies considerably in size, shape and
position. The parietal (wall) surface lies against the diaphragm and the liver; that part
around the entrance of the esophagus is termed the cardia. The visceral (gut) surface faces the intestines and pancreas.

The **esophageal region** of the stomach's mucous membrane (lining) is like that of
the esophagus. It lacks glands. The **cardiac gland region** and **pyloric gland region** contain mucous glands. Glands of the **fundic gland region** secrete hydrochlo-
ric acid and pepsin, a protein-digesting enzyme.

A pyloric sphincter muscle regulates the flow of stomach contents into the duodenum.

The bile duct and pancreatic duct empty at the **major duodenal papilla;** the accessory pancreatic duct, at the **minor duodenal papilla.**
The long, highly coiled small intestine averages around 70 feet in length.

Vomiting is very rare and inefficient in the horse apparently due to the tight caudal
esophageal sphincter muscle. Acute distension of the stomach can cause rupture
with or without vomiting.

Plate 51

Figure 1

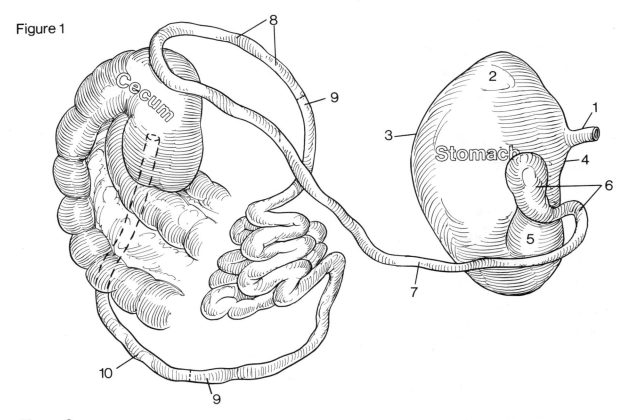

Cecum

8

9

3

2

Stomach

1

4

6

5

7

10

9

Figure 2

Esophageal region

Cardiac orifice

Esophagus

Minor duodenal papilla

Plicated margin

Cardiac gland region

Fundic gland region

Major duodenal papilla

Pylorus

Pyloric gland region

Figure 1. Schematic drawing of the isolated large intestine viewed from the right with
            parts slightly separated.
Identify the major parts of the large intestine.
Arrows indicate movement of ingested feed toward the rectum.

Cecum - receives the ileum, last part of the small intestine.
Large (ascending) colon.
    1. Right ventral colon
    2. Sternal flexure
    3. Left ventral colon
    4. Pelvic flexure
    5. Left dorsal colon
    6. Diaphragmatic flexure
    7. Right dorsal colon
Transverse colon - narrows as it leads from the large colon to the small colon.
Small (descending) colon - more folded in the living horse.
Rectum - continues caudad from the brim of pelvis, ending at the anus.
H = sacculations (haustra) of the large intestine.
T = longitudinal bands (taeniae coli) consisting mainly of smooth muscle.

Figure 2. Openings (orifices) in the base of the cecum.
A **sphincter** of smooth muscle surrounds the **ileal orifice,** providing a valve-like
action.
The **cecocolic orifice** leads into the right ventral colon.

Colic (abdominal pain) has many causes. Impaction (obstruction) by feed, meconium
(a foal's first stool) or foreign bodies is one cause of colic. Impaction is most likely to
occur where the intestine narrows: **ileal orifice, pelvic flexure** or beginning of the
transverse colon.

Plate 52

Rectum

Figure 1

Small colon

Transverse colon
Large colon

H

Base

H

Cecum

Ileum

Body

Cecocolic fold

Apex

1 2 3 4 5 6 7 T H

Figure 2

Cecocolic orifice
Ridge
Ileal orifice
Sphincter muscle
in margin

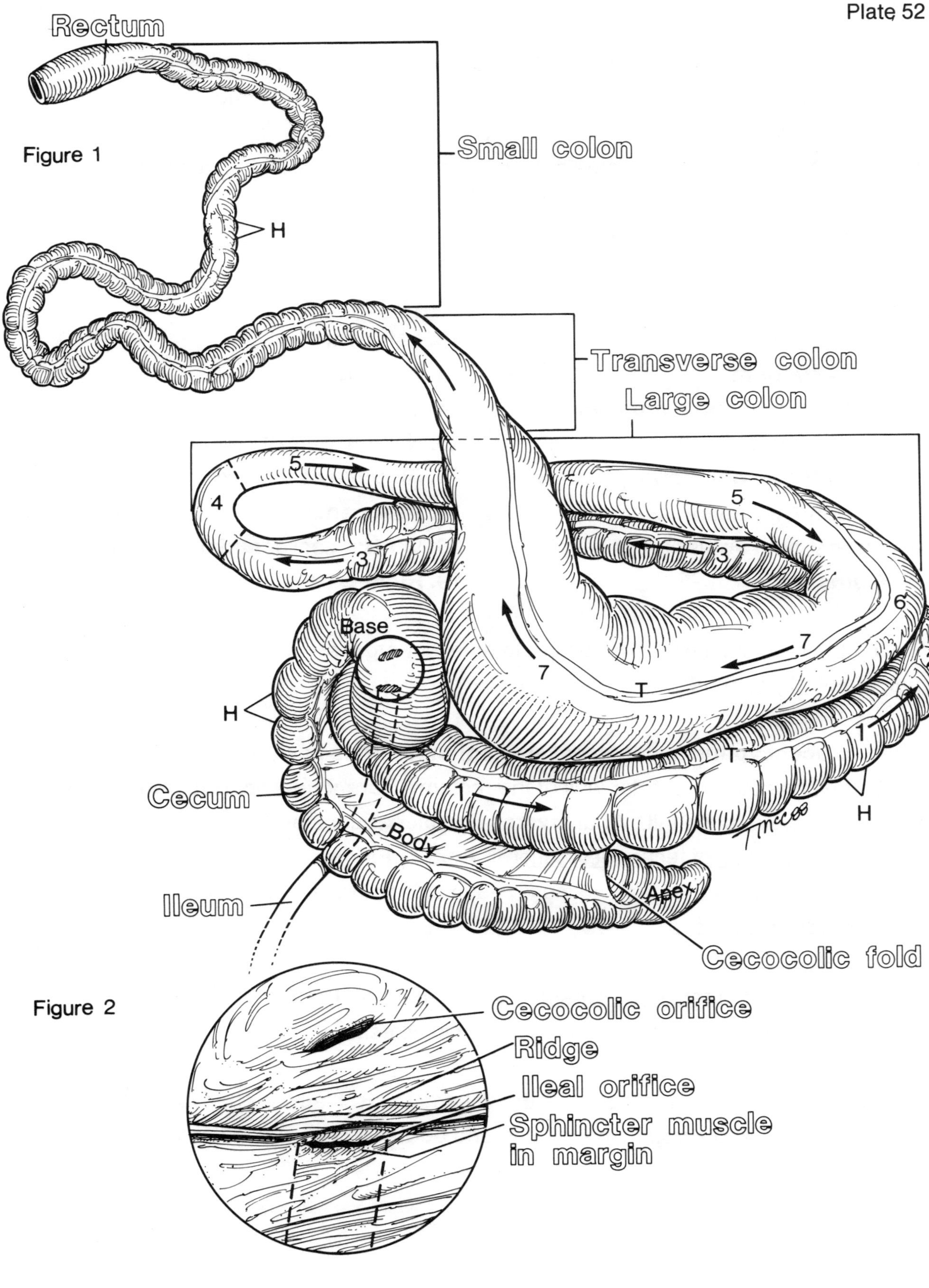

Figure 1. Lateral dissection of pelvic wall deep to the broad sacrotuberal ligament.

Figure 2. Deeper lateral dissection of female pelvic cavity and caudal part of abdominal cavity.

Figure 3. Median section of female pelvic cavity and caudal part of abdominal cavity.

Figure 4. Caudal view of dissected anus and male perineum. Thermometer through anal canal into rectum.

1. Rectum
2. Coccygeus m.
3. External anal sphincter m.
4. Anal levator m.
5. Dorsal sacrocaudal muscles
6. Rectococcygeus m.
7. Retractor m. of clitoris
   (of penis in male)
8. Internal anal sphincter m.
9. Vagina
10. Urinary bladder
11. Left horn of uterus
12. Left ovary
13. Left kidney
14. Termination of small colon
15. Narrow part of rectum
16. Ampulla of rectum
17. Anal canal
18. Ventral sacrocaudal muscles
19. Right crus of root of penis

Notice the relationships of the rectum to adjacent organs. Most of them may be palpated (felt) by a hand in the rectum.

The **rectococcygeus** and **internal anal sphincter muscles** are smooth muscle continuations of the muscular wall of the rectum. **Dorsal sacrocaudal muscles** act together to elevate the tail. **Anal levator muscles** reduce protrusion of the anus during the passage of feces (defecation). **Anal sphincter muscles** close the **anal canal**. **Coccygeus muscles** acting on each side with **ventral sacrocaudal muscles** depress the tail.

The horse's normal rectal temperature is from **99.5° to 101.5°F**. It is higher in the day than at night and higher in summer than in winter.

The perineum is the region between the tail and the ischiadic arch, especially between the anus and scrotum in the male and between the anus and vulva in the female.

Plate 53

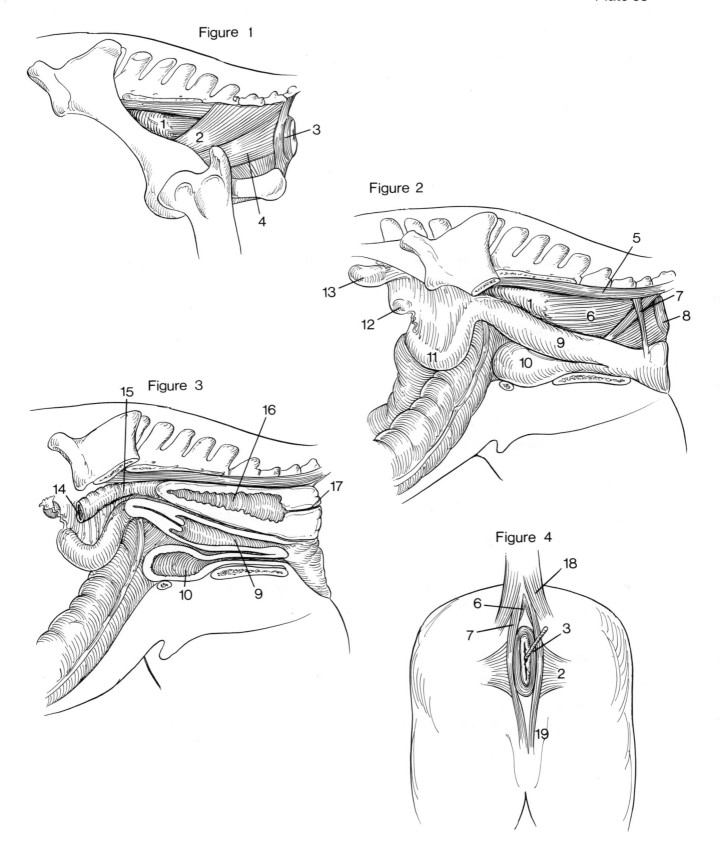

Figure 1

Figure 2

Figure 3

Figure 4

Figure 1. Diaphragmatic surface of horse's liver. Embalmed in place.
Figure 2. Visceral (gut) surface of same liver.
Figure 3. Ventral view of pancreas and related organs.

Identify the words and structures indicated on the drawings.

Peritoneal ligaments that support the liver:

1. Right triangular ligament   **3. Coronary ligament**

2. Left triangular ligament   **4. Falciform ligament**

The **liver** is the horse's largest gland with an average weight of 11 lb. Its secretion of
bile is delivered directly to the **duodenum** by the **bile duc**t, since the horse lacks a
gall bladder for storing bile. In the intestine, bile aids in the digestion of fat by breaking large globules into small globules.

Two blood vessels supply the liver:

1) The **portal vein** carries blood from the intestines to the liver's sinusoids - spaces
   between sheets of liver cells.
2) The **hepatic artery**'s branches supply needed nutrients, especially oxygen, to the
   liver's cells, eventually emptying into sinusoids.

Blood flows from sinusoids into branches of the **hepatic veins**. Hepatic veins empty
into the **caudal vena cava**.

Nutrients and other substances (for example, toxins) absorbed from the intestines
and carried to the liver by the portal vein are processed by liver cells.

The **pancreas** is two glands in one:

1) The exocrine part (secretion carried by pancreatic ducts to the duodenum)
   produces digestive enzymes.
2) The endocrine part (products secreted into the blood for transport to target tissues
   elsewhere) secretes the hormones, **insulin** and **glucagon**. These hormones are
   produced by specific cells in masses termed Islets of Langerhans. Insulin de-
   creases blood sugar (glucose); glucagon mobilizes blood sugar.

Plate 54

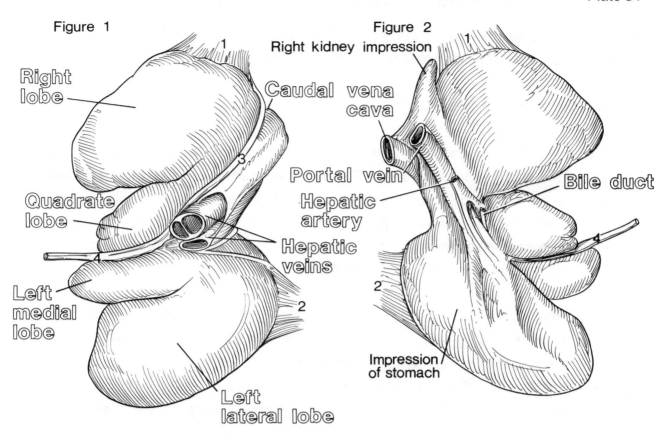

Figure 1

Right lobe

Caudal vena cava

Quadrate lobe

Hepatic artery

Hepatic veins

Left medial lobe

1

3

2

Left lateral lobe

Figure 2

Right kidney impression

Portal vein

Hepatic artery

Bile duct

Impression of stomach

1

2

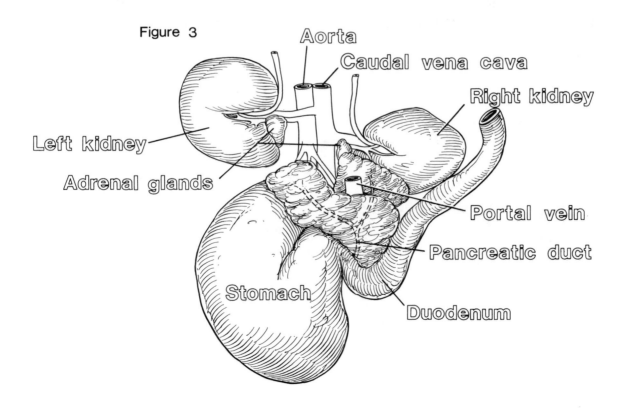

Figure 3

Aorta

Caudal vena cava

Right kidney

Left kidney

Adrenal glands

Portal vein

Pancreatic duct

Stomach

Duodenum

Figure 1. Positions of organs related to right wall of abdomen.
Figure 2. Positions of organs related to left wall of abdomen.

Identify the organs indicated.

Cellulose in feed (particularly hay and grass) is digested into absorbable nutrients by bacteria in the cecum and large colon. Gases (mainly carbon dioxide and methane) are produced as a by-product of this process. A stethoscope (or even one's ear pressed against the abdomen over parts of the large intestine) can be used to determine the presence or absence of intestinal sounds. These sounds are caused by the propulsion of gas and other fluids through the large intestine.

Horses normally produce and expel large quantities of gas. Abnormal accumulations of gas in the intestines (distension colic) may be relieved by injecting certain drugs or by giving mineral oil to help restore normal intestinal motility. A cecum greatly distended with gas may be emptied by puncturing its base through the right flank with a trocar. This instrument is a hollow metal tube with a sharp-pointed insert that is withdrawn following the puncture, allowing gas to escape. Knowing the in situ (in place) positions of organs can assist in making a diagnosis or treating a diseased organ. Keeping in mind their in situ positions helps in locating organs by a hand in the rectum.

Plate 55

Figure 1

Base of cecum   Duodenum   Right kidney   Liver

Right ventral colon

Right dorsal colon   Diaphragm

Figure 2

Diaphragm   Stomach   Spleen   Descending colon

Pelvic flexure

Liver   Left dorsal colon   Left ventral colon   Jejunum

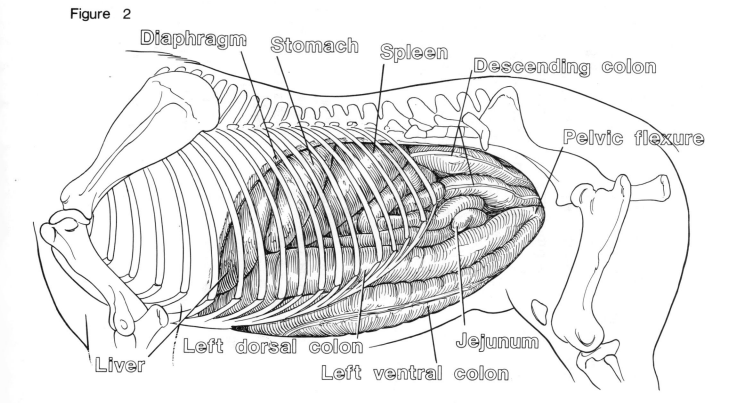

Plate 56

BODY CAVITIES AND SEROUS MEMBRANES

THORACIC, ABDOMINAL AND PELVIC CAVITIES

Diagrammatic drawing of major body cavities and serous membranes of the mare.

Peritoneum also suspends and encloses some of the male reproductive organs.

Peritoneum is divided into three continuous parts:

1. **Parietal peritoneum** - lines abdominal cavity and cranial part of pelvic cavity. (Latin, paries = walls)

2. **Connecting peritoneum** - suspends organs; double fold enclosing vessels and nerves.

   a. Mes + organ suspended: **mesentery** (Greek, mesos = middle + enteron = intestine)

        mesometrium (Greek, metra = womb)

   b. Peritoneal ligaments: suspend and support - e.g. **falciform ligament** of liver.

3. **Visceral peritoneum** - encloses a <u>viscus</u> (Latin, large, internal organ; <u>plural</u>, <u>viscera</u>).

The musculomembranous **diaphragm** is covered with peritoneum on the abdominal surface and pleura on the thoracic surface.

Pleurae - two continuous serous membranes, each forming a pleural sac:

1. **Parietal pleura** - lines each half of thoracic cavity.

2. <u>Mediastinal pleura</u> - connecting pleura on each side enclosing the <u>mediastinum</u>, a space containing the heart, esophagus, trachea, blood vessels, nerves, thymus, lymph nodes and ducts, connective tissue and fat.

3. **Visceral pleura** - encloses each lung.

Pericardium

1. **Visceral pericardium** - covers the heart (also called <u>epicardium</u>).

2. Reflection around base of heart and great vessels.

3. **Parietal pericardium** - covered by fibrous tissue and mediastinal pleura.

<u>Serous cavities</u>: peritoneal cavity, pleural cavity, pericardial cavity.

<u>Potential spaces</u> between parietal and visceral serous membranes containing lubricating <u>serous fluids</u> that increase in inflammation, e.g., <u>peritonitis</u>.

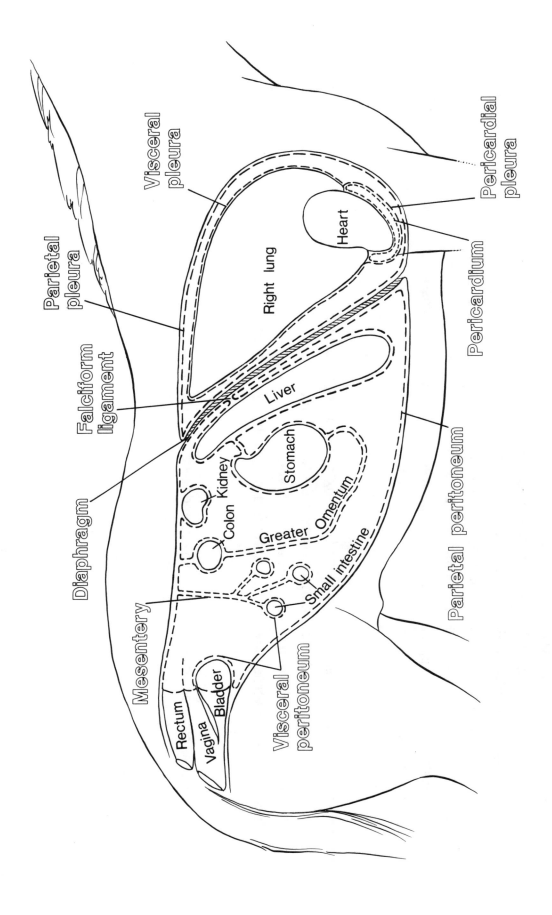

Visceral pleura

Parietal pleura

Falciform ligament

Diaphragm

Mesentery

Rectum

Vagina

Bladder

Visceral peritoneum

Heart

Right lung

Liver

Kidney

Colon

Stomach

Greater Omentum

Small intestine

Pericardial pleura

Pericardium

Parietal peritoneum

Plate 56

Plate 57

CARDIOVASCULAR SYSTEM

MAJOR VASCULAR PATTERNS

Coloring the arrows, trace the flow of poorly-oxygenated blood: (Usually colored blue.)

From the **cranial** and **caudal caval veins** to the **right atrium,**

Through the **right atrioventricular valve** to the **right ventricle,**

Out of the heart through the **pulmonary trunk valve** into the pulmonary circulation,

Through the **pulmonary trunk** and **pulmonary arteries,**

And, finally, to the capillaries (tiny vessels) in the alveoli (little sacs) in the lungs where carbon dioxide is given off and oxygen is bound to hemoglobin in the red blood cells.

Coloring return arrows a different color, trace the flow of oxygenated blood: (Usually colored red.)

From the lungs through the **pulmonary veins** to the **left atrium,**

Through the **left atrioventricular valve** to the **left ventricle,**

Then through the **aortic valve** into the **aorta** and the systemic circulation.

Notice that arteries carry blood away from the heart and veins carry blood toward the heart.

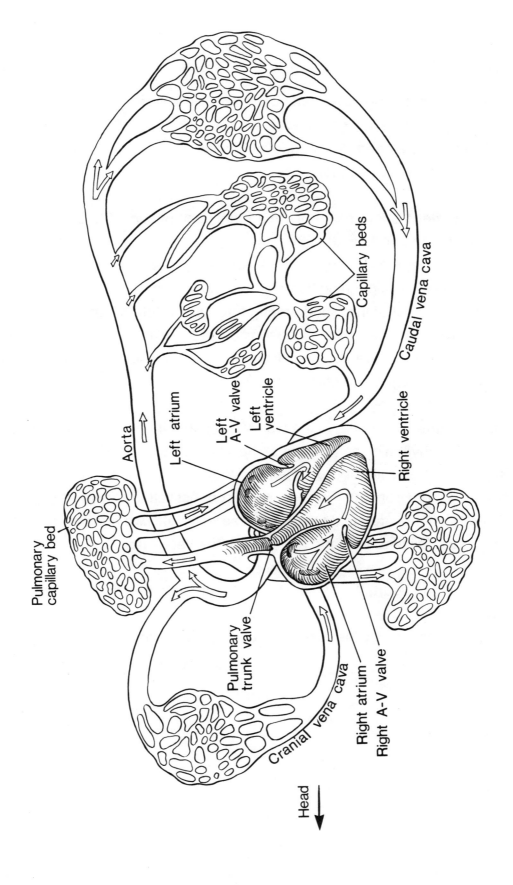

Capillary beds

Caudal vena cava

Left atrium

Left
A-V valve

Left
ventricle

Aorta

Right ventricle

Pulmonary
capillary bed

Pulmonary
trunk valve

Cranial vena cava

Right atrium

Right A-V valve

Head

Plate 57

Figure 1. Left view of the horse's heart. Coronary arteries are the first branches of
         the aorta. Left and right auricles are outpocketings of atria.
Figure 2. Section of the heart. A-V = atrioventricular; C = cusp of aortic valve;
         S = approximate location of sinoatrial node.

The **arterial ligament** is a remnant of the <u>arterial</u> <u>duct</u> that shunted blood from the
pulmonary trunk to the aorta in the <u>fetus</u> <u>(unborn foal)</u>. A depression in the wall
between the two atria, the <u>oval</u> <u>fossa</u> (not seen here), indicates the position of the
<u>oval</u> <u>foramen</u>, a valve-like opening that shunted blood from the right atrium to the left
atrium in the fetus. Most of the blood flowing through the fetal heart is shunted
through these two passages, minimizing the flow of blood into the pulmonary circulation. Since the fetal lungs are not functioning, the mare's blood in the placenta supplies the fetus with oxygen and other nutrients.

The **sinoatrial node** (S-A node) in the wall of the right atrium is the <u>pacemaker</u> and
coordinator of the rhythmic contractions of the heart. It consists of modified, impulse-
conducting heart muscle fibers (<u>Purkinje</u> <u>fibers</u>) and autonomic (definition later)
nerve endings. Fibers from the sinoatrial node connect with a similar <u>atrioventricular</u>
<u>node</u> (A-V node) in the interatrial septum (not seen here). Two bundles of these
specialized fibers descend from the A-V node to the ventricles.

<u>During</u> <u>beating</u> of the heart, the two atria fill and contract; then the two ventricles fill
and contract.
<u>Heart</u> <u>sounds</u> are caused by the rush of blood and the closing of heart valves.

Plate 58

Figure 1

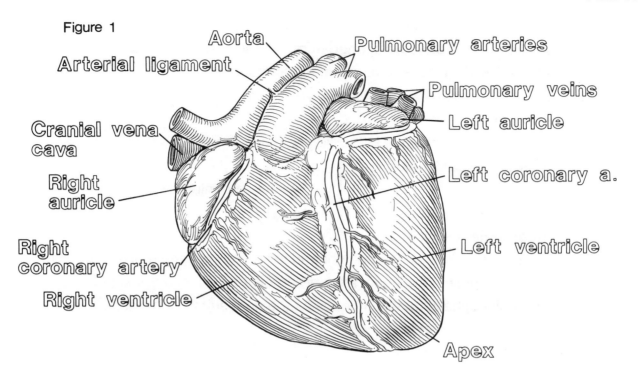

Aorta

Arterial ligament

Pulmonary arteries

Pulmonary veins

Left auricle

Cranial vena cava

Right auricle

Left coronary a.

Right coronary artery

Left ventricle

Right ventricle

Apex

Figure 2

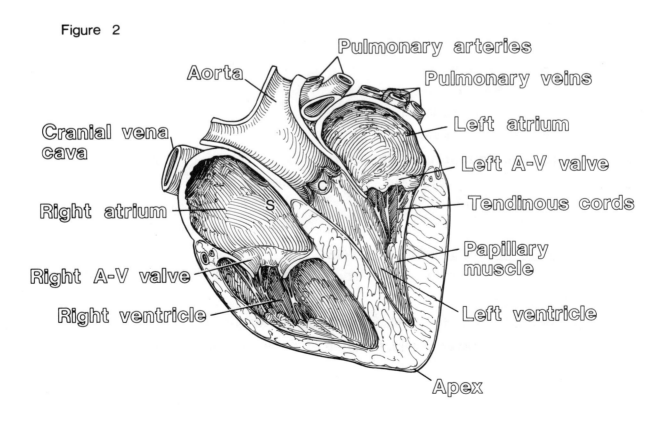

Aorta

Cranial vena cava

Right atrium

Right A-V valve

Right ventricle

Pulmonary arteries

Pulmonary veins

Left atrium

Left A-V valve

Tendinous cords

Papillary muscle

Left ventricle

Apex

Figure 1. Dissected thorax of horse opened from left side.

Figure 2. Dissected thorax of horse opened from right side. One lung, pericardium
and mediastinal pleura removed in Figures 1 and 2.

1. Aorta

   2. Brachiocephalic trunk

      3. L. subclavian a. - becomes left axillary a. beyond rib 1

         4. L. costocervical trunk

         5. L. vertebral a.   All accompanied by

         6. L. internal thoracic a.   satellite veins

         7. L. superficial cervical a.

      8. Bicarotid trunk - branches into right and left <u>common</u> <u>carotid</u> <u>arteries</u>, main
blood supply to the head. After giving off the bicarotid trunk, the
brachiocephalic trunk continues as the <u>right</u> <u>subclavian</u> <u>artery</u>.

  9. Left axillary artery and vein

 10. Branches of left vagus nerve

 11. Phrenic nerve - motor supply to diaphragm

 12. Thoracic duct

 13. Pulmonary trunk

 14. Pulmonary veins

 15. Cranial caval vein (vena cava)

 16. Right external jugular vein

 17. Right azygous vein

 18. Caudal caval vein (vena cava)

 19. Right vertebral artery and vein

 20. Left and right common carotid arteries

 21. Right axillary artery and vein - from rt. subclavian a. & v.

<u>Three</u> <u>passages</u> through the **diaphragm**, the musculomembranous <u>partition</u>
<u>between</u> <u>the</u> <u>thoracic</u> <u>and</u> <u>abdominal</u> <u>cavities</u> <u>are</u>:

22. Aortic hiatus - transmits aorta, r. azygous vein and chyle cistern (beginning of
thoracic duct)

23. Esophageal hiatus - transmits esophagus and vagus nerves

24. Foramen venae cavae (Latin, foramen of the vena cava) - transmits caudal
caval vein

Plate 59

Figure 1

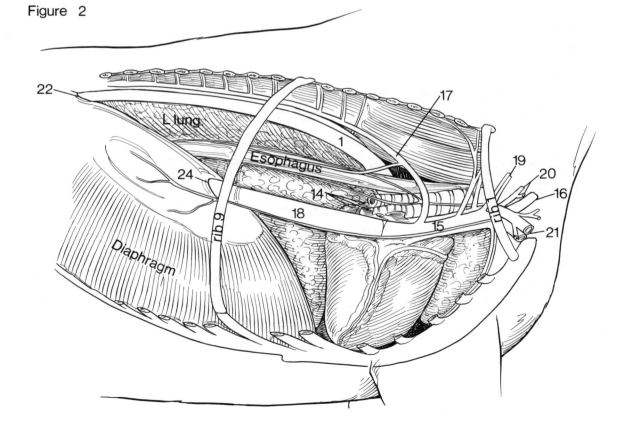

Figure 2

Schematic drawing of a ventral view of major vessels of abdominal and pelvic cavities of a mare.

1. **Aorta**
2. **Caudal caval vein (vena cava)**
3. **Celiac artery**
4. **Splenic artery**
5. **Left gastric artery**
6. **Hepatic artery**
7. **Gastroepiploic arteries**
8. **Renal artery**
9. **Renal vein**
10. **Cranial mesenteric artery**
11. **Pancreaticoduodenal, jejunal, ileal, colic and cecal arteries**

12. **Ovarian a. & v. (male testicular vessels)**
13. **Caudal mesenteric a.**
14. **Left colic a.**
15. **Cranial rectal a.**
16. **External iliac arteries**
17. **Deep circumflex iliac a. and v.**
18. **Uterine a. & v. (male cremaster vessels)**
19. **Internal iliac arteries** - branches to pelvic organs
20. **Portal vein** - to liver
21. **Hepatic veins** - from liver

Arteries from **celiac, cranial mesenteric** and **caudal mesenteric arteries** supply the stomach, spleen, intestines and pancreas. **Veins** from these organs carry blood to the liver through the **portal vein**.

The significance of the blood supply to the intestines is the concern of every horse owner! Horses should be wormed periodically (ideally every 2 to 3 months) to reduce the number of <u>blood worms (Strongyles)</u>. <u>Larvae</u> (young forms) of these worms migrate from the small intestine to the **cranial mesenteric artery** and its branches where they cause the formation of **thrombi** (<u>clots</u> on the arterial lining) and <u>aneurysms</u> (expansions) of the wall. <u>Emboli</u> (fragments of thrombi) may break off and plug smaller arteries "downstream", depriving the intestine of blood and causing death of tissue. This produces severe <u>verminous</u> (worm-caused) <u>colic.</u> Intestinal parasites can also cause <u>diarrhea</u> and <u>unthriftiness</u>. Migrating larvae produce <u>peritoneal</u> <u>adhesions</u>. Proper pasture management can help to control the ingestion of parasites by horses.

Plate 60

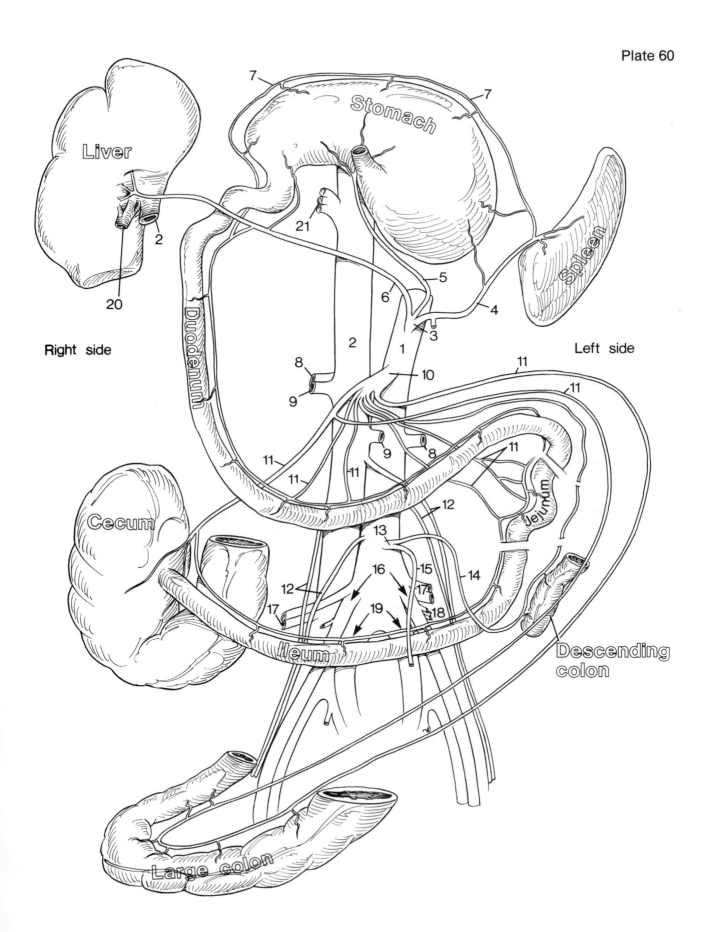

Liver

Stomach

Spleen

7

7

2

20

21

Right side

Duodenum

5

6

3

2

1

8

9

10

Left side

11

11

9

8

11

11

11

Cecum

11

12

12

13

16

15

14

Jejunum

17

17

18

12

19

17

Ileum

Descending colon

Large colon

In this diagrammatic drawing, vessels appear to be in the same plane. Actually, they are at different depths.

a.= artery; v.= vein.

1. **Common carotid a.** - main blood supply to head. Accompanied by vagosympathetic nerve trunk.
2. **Vertebral a.** - courses through transverse foramina of cervical vertebrae. Joins opposite artery to form <u>basilar a</u>., secondary blood supply to brain.
3. **Thyroid a.**
4. **Internal carotid a.** - passes through foramen lacerum. Main blood supply to brain.
5. **Occipital a.**
6. **Linguofacial trunk** - divides into lingual a. and facial a.
7. **External carotid a.** - continuation of common carotid a.
8. **Caudal auricular a.** - becomes superficial.
9. **Superficial temporal a.**
10. **Rostral auricular a.** - becomes superficial.
11. **Transverse facial a.** - becomes superficial. To masseter m.
12. **Maxillary a.** - continuation of external carotid a. Several branches: mandibular alveolar, middle meningeal, temporal aa., arteries to the eye, palatine aa., and
13. **Infraorbital a.** - into infraorbital canal. Supplies upper teeth.
14. **Mandibular alveolar a**. - to mandible and lower teeth
15. **Facial a.** - becomes superficial. Branches to face.
16. **External jugular v.** - courses down neck in the <u>jugular groove</u> between the brachiocephalic and sternomandibular muscles. Receives branches from satellite (companion) veins to the arteries and from dural venous sinuses (in fibrous covering of brain). Carries blood to cranial caval vein.

Plate 61

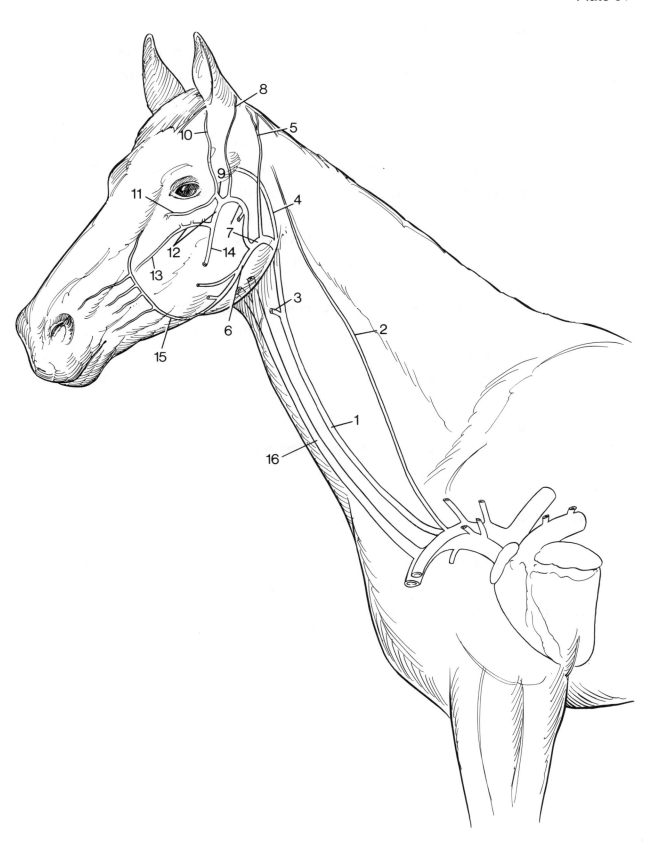

The pulse is the rhythmic expansion of arteries due to the beating heart forcing blood into the vessels. The pulse may be felt through the skin over certain arteries. By pressing the finger tips down and then lifting up slightly, the pulse may be taken at these sites.

Figure 1. **A. Facial artery**. Place the thumb on the fullest part of the jaw and rub the finger tips along the ventral border of the mandible to feel the artery.
B. Transverse facial artery. Place finger tips caudal to the lateral canthus of the eyelids and ventral to the zygomatic arch.

Figure 2. **Lateral dorsal metatarsal artery.** On a hindlimb, place finger tips over the artery in the dorsal groove between the third and fourth metatarsal bones.

Figure 3. **Digital arteries.** Grasp the fetlock dorsally with the fingers extending to the pastern. Place the thumb over the lateral digital artery and curl the fingers around the medial side of the pastern over the medial digital artery. The digital arteries are parallel to the edges of the easily felt deep digital flexor tendon. This pulse may be felt on the digits of the hindlimb as well.

Normal pulse rate for a horse at rest is from 28 to 40 pulses per minute. This reflects the heart rate. Following moderate exercise, the heart rate will increase from 180 to 240 beats per minute. It should return to around 60 beats per minute at rest in 10 to 15 minutes and then slowly decrease to the normal rate. A very rapid or very slow pulse (heart) rate in the resting horse indicates disease.

Of the sites described above, the pulse in the digital arteries is often the most difficult to feel unless inflammation exists in the foot. Acute laminitis - inflammation of the dermal (sensitive) laminae - causes increased, strong pulsation in the digital arteries.

Plate 62

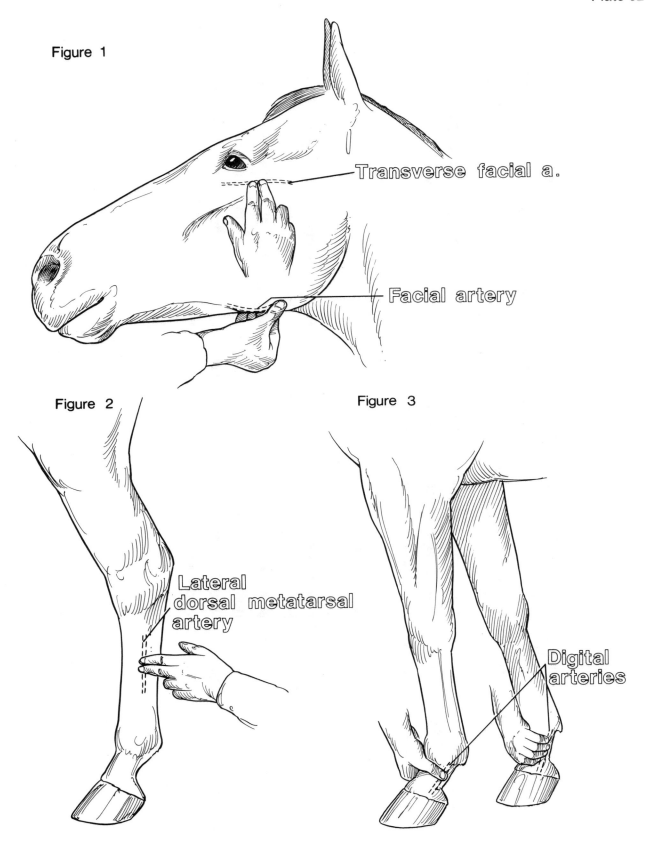

Figure 1

Transverse facial a.

Facial artery

Figure 2

Lateral dorsal metatarsal artery

Figure 3

Digital arteries

Plate 63

HEMICLYMPHATIC SYSTEM

BONE MARROW, THYMUS AND SPLEEN

Red marrow produces red blood cells and many of the white blood cells (mainly granulated cells) and cell fragments called platelets. The latter are essential for blood clotting. **Yellow marrow** consists primarily of fat cells, but blood cell-producing units may begin producing blood cells again.

At first bluish, the **spleen** becomes reddish brown when exposed to air due to the blood-engorged red pulp. The storage-type spleen of the horse has a capsule containing smooth muscle that contracts to move blood out of the spleen into the circulation. When the muscle is relaxed, the volume of the spleen increases.

The spleen's masses of white pulp produce lymphocytes.

A peritoneal **gastrosplenic ligament** extends from the stomach to the spleen and a **renosplenic ligament** from the left kidney to the spleen. Parts of the large colon may be displaced through or over these peritoneal ligaments. The **thymus** of the foal is largest at six to eight weeks of age, occupying the cranial part of the mediastinum and extending craniad through the thoracic inlet and into the neck next to the trachea. The thymus produces T-lymphocytes (T-cells) that will populate other hemiclymphatic organs. As the animal ages, the thymus becomes smaller and smaller until it is finally a small mass surrounded by fat and connective tissue in the cranial mediastinum.

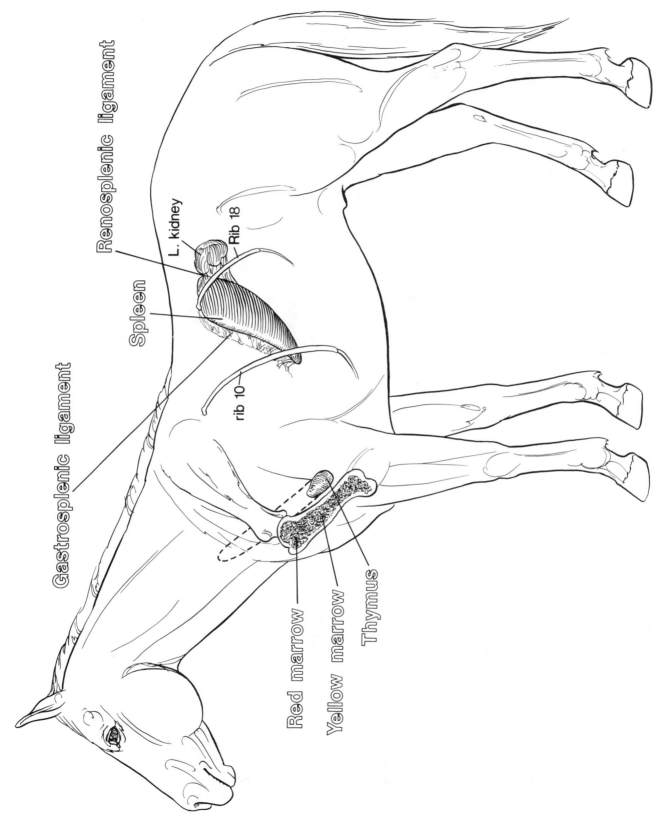

Renosplenic ligament

Gastrosplenic ligament

L. kidney

Rib 18

Spleen

rib 10

Red marrow

Yellow marrow

Thymus

Plate 63

Plate 64

LYMPH NODES AND LYMPH VESSELS

Lc = <u>lymphocenter</u>; Inn = <u>lymph nodes</u>. Dashed lines indicate lymphatics (lymph vessels).

1. **Mandibular Lc**

2. **Parotid Lc**

3. **Retropharyngeal Lc**

4. **Deep cervical Lc**
   Cranial, middle and caudal deep cervical Inn

5. **Left tracheal trunk**

6. **Superficial cervical Lc**

7. **Right lymphatic duct**

8. **Dorsal thoracic Lc**

9. **Thoracic duct**
   Empties into cranial vena cava or left jugular vein.

10. **Bronchial Lc** - Tracheobronchial Inn   Pulmonary Inn

11. **Mediastinal Lc**
    Cranial, middle and caudal mediastinal Inn

12. **Ventral thoracic Lc** - Sternal Inn

13. **Axillary Lc** - Proper axillary Inn   Cubital Inn

14. **Chyle cistern** - Receives lymphatic trunk.
    Origin of thoracic duct.

15. **Celiac Lc**
    Celiac Inn   Hepatic Inn
    Gastric Inn   Splenic Inn   Pancreaticoduodenal Inn

16. **Cranial mesenteric Lc**
    Cranial mesenteric Inn   Cecal Inn
    Jejunal Inn   Colic Inn

17. **Lumbar Lc** - Lumbar aortic Inn   Renal Inn

18. **Caudal mesenteric Lc**

19. **Iliosacral Lc**
    Medial iliac Inn   Lateral iliac Inn
    Internal iliac Inn   Sacral Inn   Anorectal Inn

20. **Lumbar trunk(s)**

21. **Intestinal trunk(s)**

22. **Inguinofemoral Lc**
    Subiliac Inn   Superficial inguinal Inn

23. **Iliofemoral (deep inguinal) Lc**

24. **Popliteal Lc**

<u>Tissue fluid</u> = <u>source of lymph</u>, the fluid in lymph vessels (lymphatics).

<u>Stocking-up:</u> Tissue fluid swells a horse's lower limbs due to the lack of exercise needed to force the upward flow of lymph. May occur when hard worked horses are stabled overnight.

<u>Phagocytes</u> (<u>cell-eating cells</u>) in lymph nodes can remove bacteria and cancer cells.

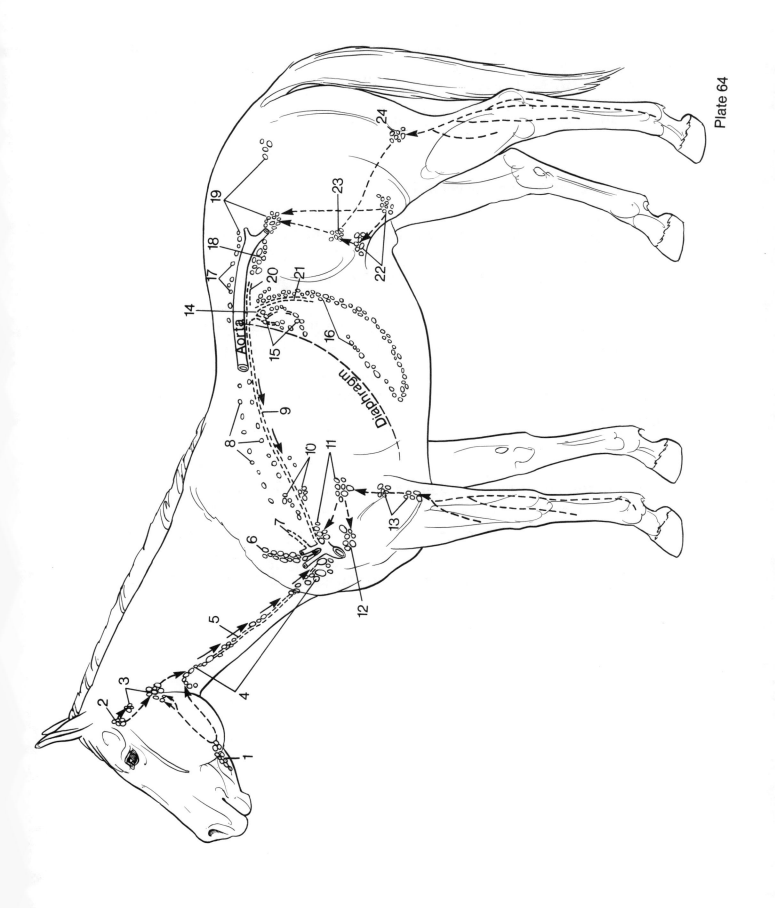

Aorta

Diaphragm

Plate 64

NASAL CAVITY, NASOPHARYNX AND LARYNX

Figure 1. Sagittal section of interior of nasal cavity, nasopharynx and larynx. For a view of the nasal septum, see Plate 50.
Arrow = entrance to auditory tube.
Dashed line = extent of laryngeal ventricle

The **dorsal meatus**, **middle meatus** and **ventral meatus** open into a <u>common meatus</u> limited medially by the <u>nasal septum</u>, a partition of cartilage and bone that divides the nasal cavity into halves. The ventral meatus is the largest. The **vomeronasal organs** are two long tubes of cartilage lined with mucous membrane that course caudad from the incisve ducts (extending in from each ventral meatus) on each side of the vomer bone along the floor of the ventral meatus.
 A <u>nasogastric tube</u> (stomach tube) inserted through the nostril is pushed along the ventral meatus, then slides over the soft palate and passes through the nasopharynx into the esophagus.

Figure 2. Flehmen stance of a stallion.
In the flehmen response, the upward-turned upper lip partially closes the nostrils, creating suction in the incisive ducts that draws fluids into the vomeronasal organs. Better analysis of nonvolatile compounds in mucus is accomplished by stimulation of olfactory nerve endings in the mucous membrane.   Flehmen behavior is pro-nounced in stallions investigating the urine and vaginal secretions of mares in heat.

Plate 65

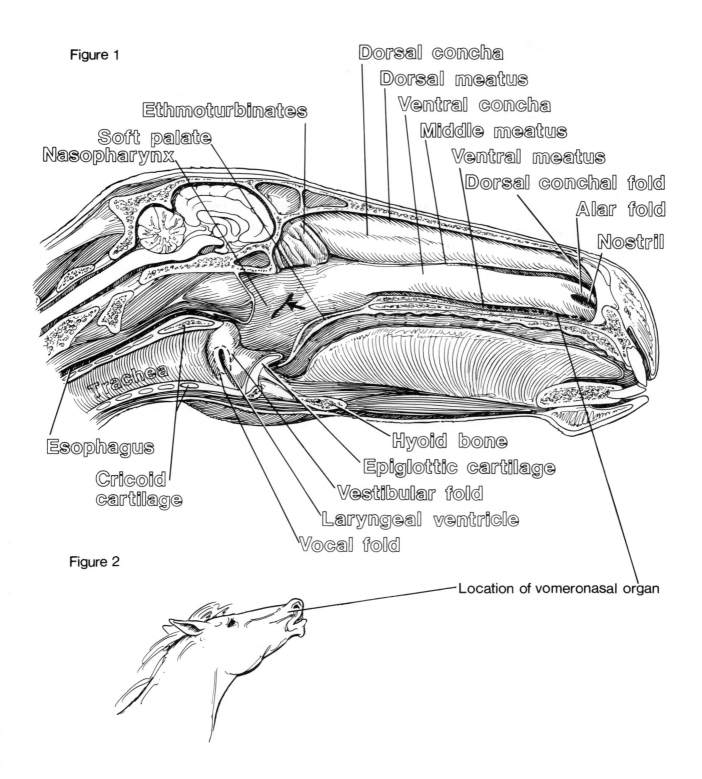

Figure 1

Dorsal concha
Dorsal meatus
Ventral concha
Middle meatus
Ventral meatus
Dorsal conchal fold
Alar fold
Nostril

Ethmoturbinates
Soft palate
Nasopharynx

Trachea

Esophagus

Cricoid
cartilage

Hyoid bone
Epiglottic cartilage
Vestibular fold
Laryngeal ventricle
Vocal fold

Figure 2

Location of vomeronasal organ

Figure 1. Right lateral view of laryngeal cartilages.
Figure 2. Right lateral view of laryngeal muscles. Wing of thyroid cartilage cut away.
Figure 3. Rostrocaudal view of larynx. X = **rima** (cleft) **of the glottis**, the walls of
    which are formed by the **vocal folds** and parts of the **arytenoid cartilages**.

1. Cricoid cartilage	**10. Dorsal cricoarytenoid m.**
2. Arytenoid cartilage(s)	**11. Lateral cricoarytenoid m.**
3. Thyroid foramen	**12. Transverse arytenoid m.**
4. Epiglottic cartilage	**13. Hyoepiglottic muscle**
5. Thyrohyoid bone	**14. Ventricular muscle**
6. Thyroid cartilage	**15. Laryngeal ventricle**
7. Cricothyroid membrane	**16. Vocal m.** (in vocal fold)
Spreads between thyroid wings	**17. Cricothyroid muscle**
8. Cricotracheal membrane	**18. Vocal fold (cord)**
9. Tracheal rings	**19. Vestibular fold**

Functions of the larynx:
1. Regulates the volume of air entering the trachea.
2. Prevents foreign material from entering the larynx.
3. Phonation (vocal sounds).

 On each side, a **cranial laryngeal nerve** (from the vagus n.) supplies the
cricothyroid m. and then goes through the **thyroid foramen** to provide sensation to
the laryngeal mucous membrane.
Caudal laryngeal nerves - terminations of the recurrent laryngeal nerve that as-
cends the neck from the vagus in the thorax supply all the other laryngeal muscles.

"Roarer": When a recurrent laryngeal nerve degenerates (mainly the left nerve),
paralysis of the **dorsal cricoarytenoid muscle** lets the **arytenoid cartilage** and the
vocal fold move inward to interfere with the flow of air during inspiration. The **laryngeal ventricle** fills with air, causing a "roaring" sound. A horse so afflicted is called a
"roarer". There is some indication that this condition may be inherited.

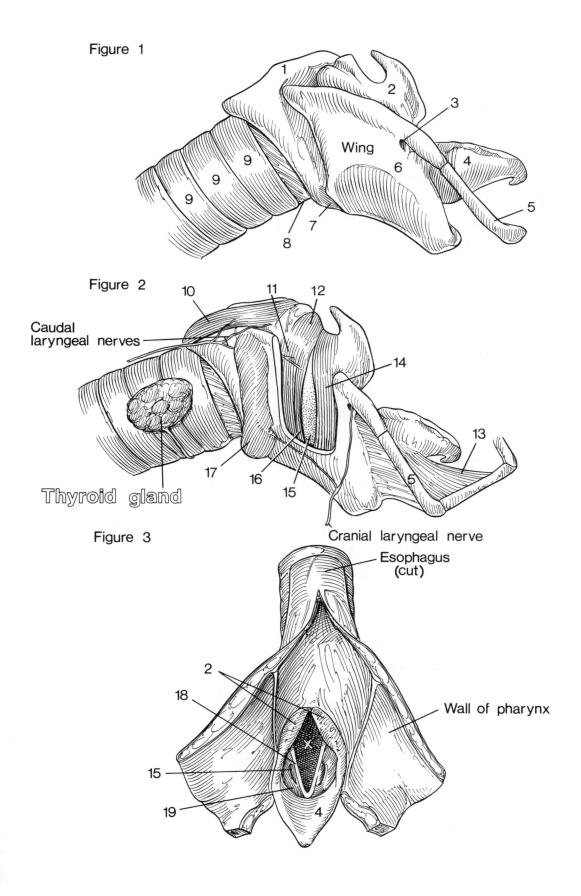

Plate 66

Figure 1

1
2
3
Wing
6
4
5
9
9
9
7
8

Figure 2

Caudal
laryngeal nerves

10
11
12
14
13
17
16
15
5

Thyroid gland

Cranial laryngeal nerve

Figure 3

Esophagus
(cut)

2
18
15
19
4

Wall of pharynx

Figure 1. Dorsal view of **trachea** and **lungs**. Diagrammatic drawing of **bronchial tree** in left lung.

Figure 2. Cross section of a cartilaginous **tracheal ring**.

Figure 3. Microscopic view of **alveoli** (little hollows), tiny air sacs with capillaries in their walls.

The 50 to 60 cartilaginous rings of the horse's trachea form incomplete hoops opening dorsally. The free ends overlap in the cervical part of the trachea, but in the thoracic part, they gradually fail to overlap. Smooth muscle fibers of the **tracheal muscle** join the inner surface of the free ends of the cartilaginous rings. Extra cartilaginous plates at the fork of the trachea fill in the gaps between the free ends of the main rings. Irregular plates support the left and right **principal bronchi** going to the lungs.

The conducting airways of the bronchial tree divide into smaller and smaller bronchi. When cartilaginous plates are no longer present in the walls of the smallest bronchi, the airway is termed a bronchiole. Terminal bronchioles lead to **respiratory bronchioles** of respiratory units. Exchange of oxygen and carbon dioxide takes place between air within alveoli and blood within capillaries in the alveolar walls. Ciliated epithelium lines most of the airways (beginning in the nasal cavity).

The normal breathing rate of a standing horse at rest is 10 to 14 breaths per minute. The rate may be affected by excitement, exercise, age, size, environmental temperature, pregnancy and/or a full digestive tract. The health of the horse also affects the breathing rate, usually increasing in disease.

Prolonged exposure to dust and molds often results in heaves or broken wind, a chronic inflammation of the airways and overdistension and rupture of alveoli (emphysema). A "heavey" horse coughs a lot, breathes loudly and has a double expiratory effort. A heave line is formed by increased musculature along the costal arch.

Plate 67

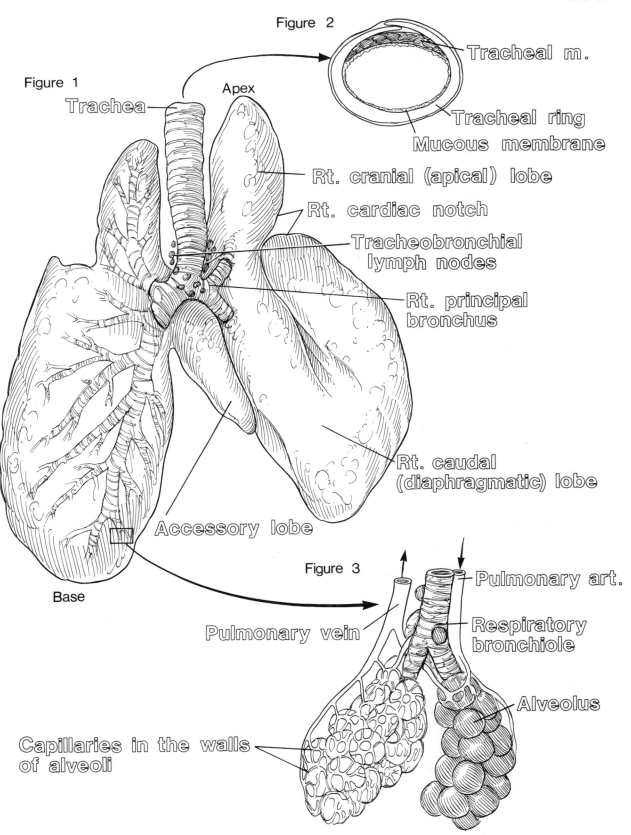

Figure 2

Tracheal m.

Figure 1

Apex

Trachea

Tracheal ring
Mucous membrane

Rt. cranial (apical) lobe

Rt. cardiac notch

Tracheobronchial
lymph nodes

Rt. principal
bronchus

Rt. caudal
(diaphragmatic) lobe

Accessory lobe

Base

Figure 3

Pulmonary art.

Pulmonary vein

Respiratory
bronchiole

Alveolus

Capillaries in the walls
of alveoli

KIDNEYS, URETERS, BLADDER AND URETHRA

Figure 1. Ventral view of urinary organs of the horse.
Figure 2. Frontal section of **right kidney**.

The tubules of the kidney produce urine by removing waste products from the great volume of blood flowing through the organ. Collecting ducts open on the **renal crest**, emptying urine into the **pelvis** of the kidney. The pelvis is essentially the expanded beginning of the **ureter**.

Urine contains the products of nitrogen and sulfur metabolism (Metabolism - processing substances, mainly nutrients, by the various tissues of the body), inorganic salts and pigments.

Normal equine urine is -
1) Somewhat thick and syrupy due to the presence of mucus secreted by mucous glands in the pelvis and first part of each ureter.
2) Cloudy due mainly to the presence of suspended calcium carbonate crystals. If a urine sample is allowed to stand, these crystals settle out.
3) Colored yellow to orange.

Volume of urine excreted -
A horse weighing around 1000 lb. voids from 1 1/2 to 8 1/2 quarts of urine daily. The volume depends on the quantity of water consumed, type of feed, amount of work and the environmental temperature.

Plate 68

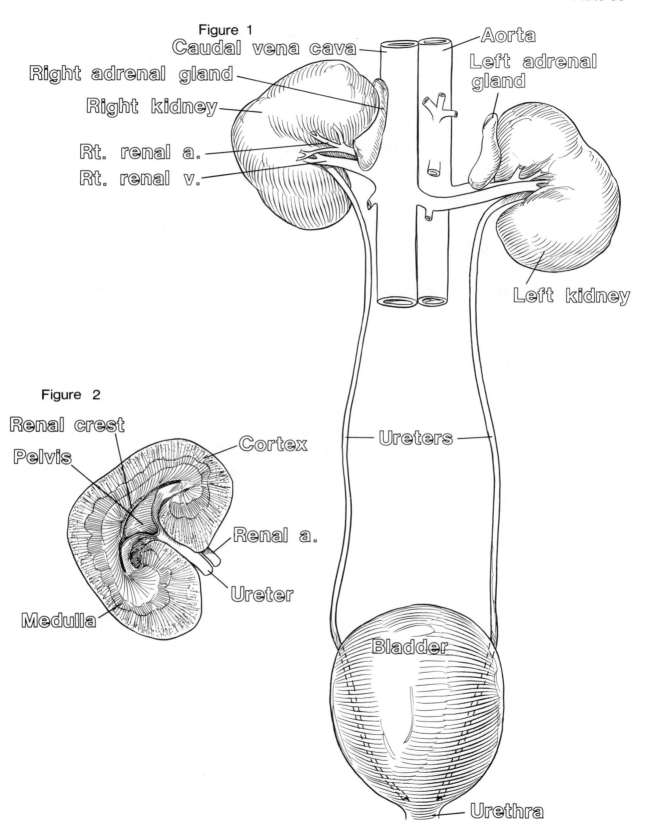

Figure 1

Caudal vena cava — Aorta

Right adrenal gland — Left adrenal gland

Right kidney

Rt. renal a.

Rt. renal v.

Left kidney

Figure 2

Renal crest — Cortex

Pelvis

Renal a.

Ureter

Medulla

Ureters

Bladder

Urethra

VULVA AND VAGINA. UDDER

Figure 1. Caudal view of **vulva** and female perineum. **Vulvar labia** (Latin, lips) parted.

Figure 2. Dorsal view of opened vulva and **vagina** (L., sheath). Bladder displaced to one side.

Figure 3. A. **Lactating udder.** B. Sagittal section of one-half.

Labia and **clitoris**, homolog (corresponding organ) of the penis, comprise the **vulva**. The **vestibule** is considered part of the vagina. Mucous glands and, on each side, an erectile vestibular bulb are present in the walls of the vestibule. Depressions in the clitoral skin contain smegma and perhaps harmful bacteria.
Constrictor muscles act on the vestibule and the vulva. In addition to constricting the vulvar opening, the constrictor of the vulva elevates the clitoris. Following urination, movement of the labia and clitoris aid in expelling the last drops of urine. During heat (estrus), quick opening and closing of the labia and elevation of the clitoris is called winking.

The mare's **udder** consist of halves, each half consisting of a cranial and a caudal gland complex and lactiferous duct system. The cranial gland and duct system is the larger. A **gland cistern** and a **teat cistern** are parts of the lactiferous sinus of each duct system. The teat from each half of the udder has two (sometimes three) openings of **streak canals**, one caudal to the other. A nonlactating udder is small with llaterally flattened teats.Wrinkled skin in the groove between the halves is covered with dark smegma that can be peeled away.

Colostrum (first milk) is produced during the final part of pregnancy.The foal can absorb immunogobulins (anitbodies) in the colostrum produced by the mare within the first 8 to 12 hours after birth. Both the production of colostrum and its abosorption taper off rapidly from birth to 12 hours.
The average-size mare produces from 9 to 11 qt. of milk daily. Milk fat in mare's milk is low (1.8% early to 1.4% late in lactation); lactose (milk sugar)is quite high (6.2% early to 6.5% later). These amounts are important when preparing a mare's milk substitute for an orphan foal. The orphan must be fed frequently - every 2 to 3 hours.

Plate 69

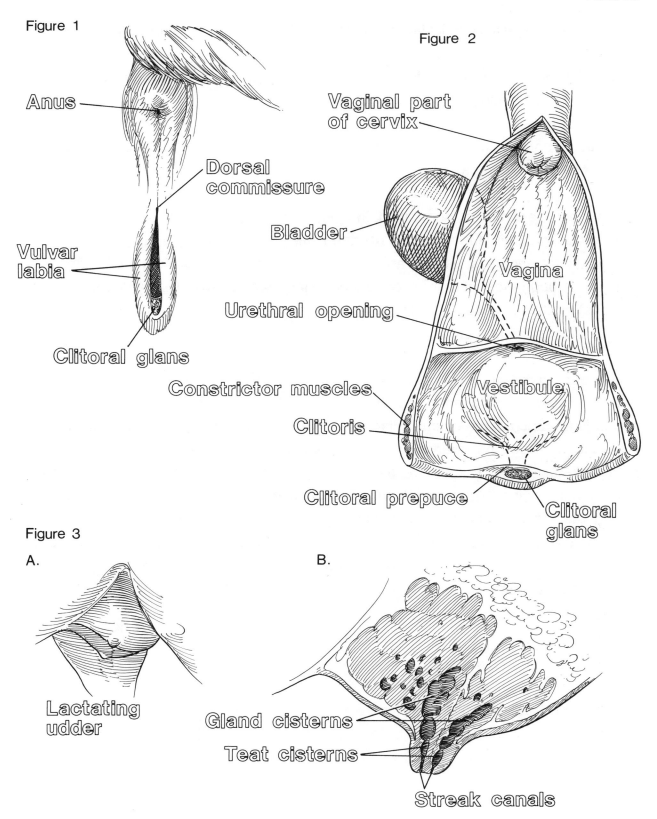

Figure 1

Anus

Dorsal commissure

Vulvar labia

Clitoral glans

Figure 2

Vaginal part of cervix

Bladder

Urethral opening

Constrictor muscles

Clitoris

Clitoral prepuce

Vagina

Vestibule

Clitoral glans

Figure 3

A.

Lactating udder

B.

Gland cisterns

Teat cisterns

Streak canals

Figure 1. A. Dorsal view of isolated female reproductive organs. B. Enlarged view of
        ovary and **uterine tube**.
Figure 2. Frontolateral view of female reproductive organs and associated structures
        with intestinal mass removed.

The **uterus** consists of four parts - **cervix** (Latin for neck), **body** (Latin, corpus) and
two **horns** (Latin, cornua). The cervix of the uterus protrudes into the vagina.

The mare's ovary has an indentation, the ovulation fossa. It is covered by the
infundibulum (Latin, funnel) of the **uterine tube** (oviduct, salpinx, Fallopian tube).
Ova (Latin for eggs) leave the ovary at the ovulation fossa, pass into the infundibulum and through the rest of the uterine tube to the **uterine horn**. Cilia (waving pro-
jections) on the lining cells and smooth muscle in the wall move ova through the
uterine tube to the end of the uterine horn.

The **broad ligament** (mesovarium + mesosalpinx + mesometrium) is connecting
peritoneum suspending the ovary, uterine tube and uterus. In the mare, the **uterine
artery** is a branch of the external iliac artery. The **ovarian artery** arises directly from
the aorta. It divides into ovarian and uterine branches. The Greek word, metra,
means uterus (Latin). Endometrium is the lining of the uterus. Endometritis is inflammation of this lining. Metritis is inflammation of the entire uterine wall. Contagious
equine metritis is caused by a bacterium that can be isolated from sinuses (depressions) in the clitoral glans. The reproductive tract of stallions is also affected. Horses
imported from several countries are quarantined for this disease before being admit-
ted to the United States.

Plate 70

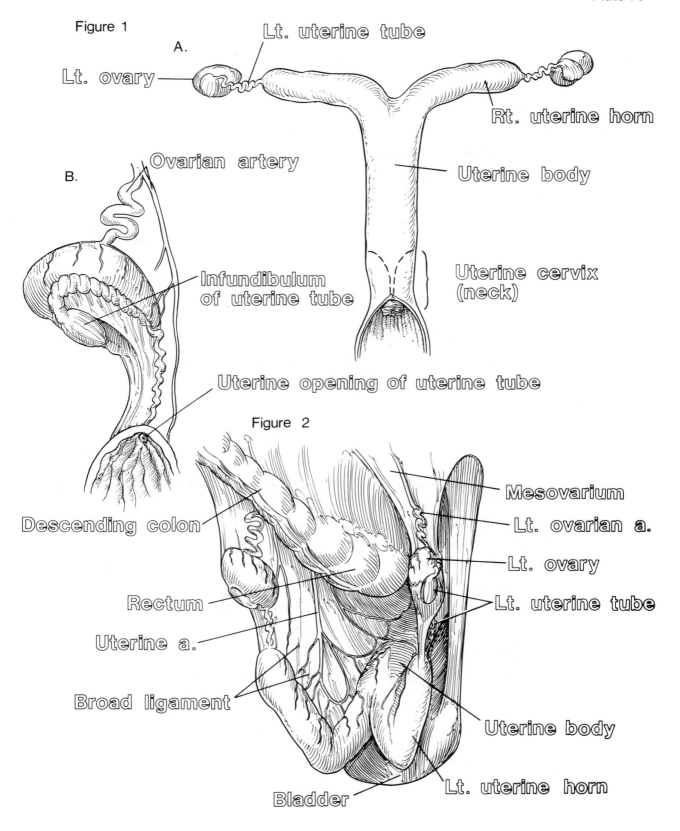

Figure 1

A.

Lt. uterine tube

Lt. ovary

Rt. uterine horn

Uterine body

B.

Ovarian artery

Infundibulum of uterine tube

Uterine cervix (neck)

Uterine opening of uterine tube

Figure 2

Descending colon

Rectum

Uterine a.

Broad ligament

Mesovarium

Lt. ovarian a.

Lt. ovary

Lt. uterine tube

Uterine body

Lt. uterine horn

Bladder

Color the open words and the structures indicated and relate the notes on the drawing to the text below.

Estrous cycles are recurring periods of heat (estrus) when the mare will mate with a stallion. Mares are seasonally polyestrous. They have several estrous cycles during a breeding season that lasts from April to October in the Northern hemisphere.
Duration of each estrous cycle ranges from 19 to 22 days. Ponies and donkeys have longer estrous cycles - around 25 days.
Estrus (follicular phase) usually lasts 5 to 7 days, but periods of 2 to 12 days can occur. The length of estrus appears to be repeatable for individual mares.
Ovulation (release of the egg cell) occurs 24 to 48 hours before the mare refuses to accept the stallion.
Diestrus (luteal phase) is the rest of the estrous cycle, lasting an average of 14 to 15 days.

Changes in behavior and in the functional anatomy of the reproductive tract during estrus and diestrus are stimulated by events in the **ovarian cycle**:
1. Initiation of estrous cycles is triggered by increasing periods of daylight stimulating the hypothalamus of the brain to secrete gonadotropin releasing hormone (GnRH). (Ovaries and testicles are gonads.)
2. GnRH causes secretion of follicle stimulating hormone (FSH) by the pituitary gland.
3. FSH stimulates the maturation of a **developing ovarian follicle** into a **Graafian follicle,** the source of the hormone, estrogen. FSH formation and release are decreased by inhibin produced by cells in the Graafian follicle.
4. Estrogen prepares the reproductive tract for mating and fertilization (union of the stallion's spermatozoon with the mare's ovum). Estrogen also stimulates the secretion of luteinizing hormone (LH) by the pituitary gland.
5. LH causes final development of the dominant Graafian follicle, ovulation (release of the egg cell), and formation of the **corpus luteum** (Latin, yellow body) (CL). The CL develops through the transformation of follicular cells in the site of the shortlived, bloody **corpus hemorrhagicum** that occurs in the follicle following ovulation.
6. Progesterone produced by the CL turns off sexual desire and prepares the reproductive tract for the embryo as it moves through the uterine tube to the uterus.
7. Prostaglandin F_{2a} (PGF_{2a}) produced by the uterus causes regression of the corpus luteum.
8. The **corpus albicans** (Latin, white body) is a scar at the site of the corpus luteum.

Plate 71

OVARIAN CYCLE

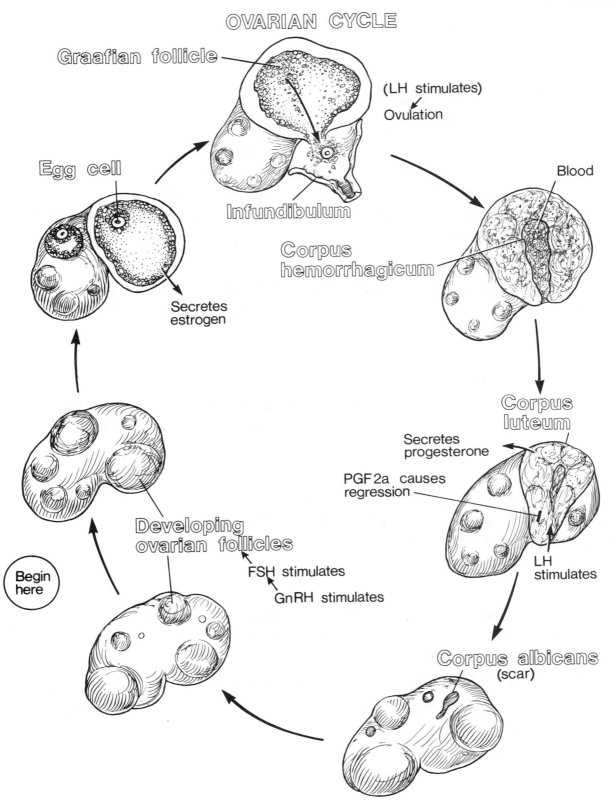

Graafian follicle

(LH stimulates)
Ovulation

Egg cell

Infundibulum

Blood

Secretes estrogen

Corpus hemorrhagicum

Corpus luteum

Secretes progesterone

PGF2a causes regression

LH stimulates

Developing ovarian follicles

FSH stimulates

GnRH stimulates

Begin here

Corpus albicans (scar)

Figure 1. Embryo and embryonic membranes on day 25 of pregnancy.

Figure 2. Embryo and embryonic membranes on day 36 of pregnancy.

Figure 3. Equine fetus and mature fetal membranes.

       Inset: Detail of placental attachment.

E = embryo; F = fetus; arrows = growth of allantois.

In early pregnancy, the **yolk sac** from the midgut of the embryo forms the **yolk sac placenta** with the endometrium of the mare's uterus. As the **allantois** grows out from the hindgut and fuses with the **chorion** and **amnion**, the **allantoic cavity** fills with a larger volume of fluid than the fluid in the **amniotic cavity**.

Around day 36 of pregnancy, girdle cells from the **chorionic girdle** invade the endometrium. These cells multiply and transform into cup cells in placental outgrowths called **endometrial cups.** Cup cells secrete equine Chorionic Gonadotropin (eCG), a hormone that stimulates estrogen production by the corpus luteum. Growth and hormone production by fetal gonads may also be stimulated by eCG. Endometrial cups are most active from day 55 to day 65 of pregnancy. An immune response from the mare causes degeneration and sloughing of endometrial cups. They are gone by day 100 to day 130.

The horse has a diffuse, epitheliochorial, adeciduate placenta. Chorionic cells contact endometrial lining cells throughout the placenta (except in the **cervical star** opposite the internal opening of the cervix). When the placenta is expelled, there is no loss of maternal tissue and very little bleeding.

The **umbilical cord** contains two arteries, a vein and the urachus, a tube extending from the fetal bladder to the allantoic cavity. Blood vessels course throughout the allantochorion.

Fetal blood in capillaries in the tiny **microcotyledons** of the allantochorion is separated from maternal blood in capillaries in the endometrium by six layers of tissue.

Hippomanes are soft, brown or white floating masses of organic material and minerals deposited on some cellular debris in the allantoic fluid. They are normal features.

Plate 72

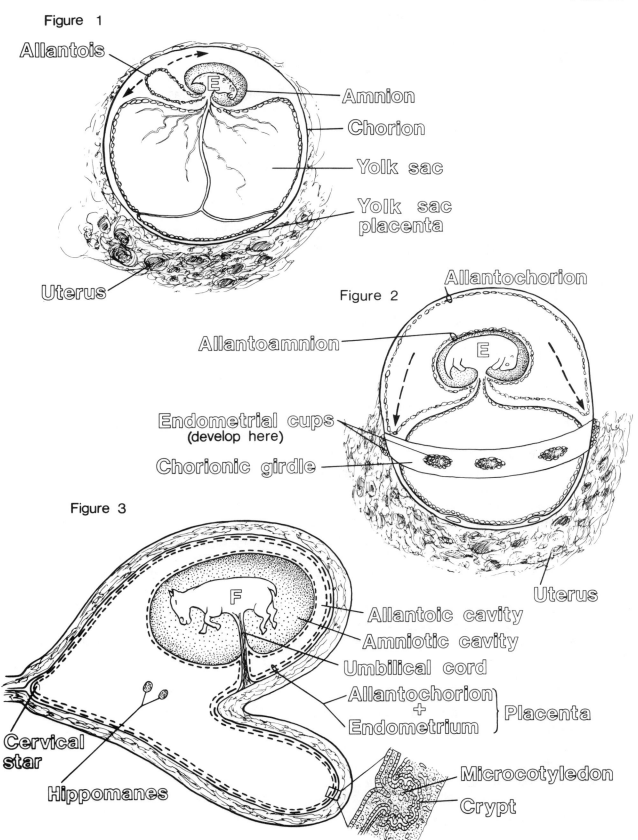

Figure 1

Allantois

Amnion

Chorion

Yolk sac

Yolk sac placenta

Uterus

E

Figure 2

Allantochorion

Allantoamnion

Endometrial cups (develop here)

Chorionic girdle

Uterus

E

Figure 3

Cervical star

Hippomanes

Allantoic cavity

Amniotic cavity

Umbilical cord

Allantochorion
+
Endometrium } Placenta

Microcotyledon

Crypt

F

Figure 1. Signs of impending parturition.
Figure 2. Cranial presentation of foal during delivery.
Figure 3. Normal expelled placenta spread out on a flat surface.

Length of the gestation period (duration of pregnancy) in the mare: 335 to 342 days.
    Extremes range from 305 to 400 days.

Signs of impending parturition, the process of giving birth:
1. Enlarged and dropped abdomen. Some ventral tissue fluid.
2. Sinking in at paralumbar fossa.
3. Relaxation and softening of muscles and ligaments adjacent to the tailhead. Softening of cervix and vulva.
4. Filling of udder with colostrum. Waxing of teats due to excessive secretion by oil glands at openings. Usually occurs around 48 hours before parturition.

Three stages of parturition:
Stage I - Onset of labor
    At first, foal is upside down (dorsopubic position).
    Mare is restless - paces, lies down and gets up, sweats in patches as early as 4 hours before delivery.
    No straining, but uterine muscular activity increases.
    Foal rolls over to upright (dorsosacral position) with its head and forelimbs extended toward the cervix.
    Cervix dilates until it is even with the vaginal wall.

Stage II - Delivery of foal
    "Water breaks" - Allantochorion ruptures and allantoic fluid passes through vulva. If intact allantochorion appears first, it should be broken at once.
    Stretched tissues cause strong contractions of abdominal muscles and the diaphragm.
    Allantoamnion appears. Mare lies on her side.
    Groups of expulsive contractions occur. Mare may get up and change position.
    One forelimb and then the other appear. Strongest contractions occur to force the head and shoulders through the mare's pelvic cavity. When the foal's hips clear the vagina, straining stops.
    Time for Stage II: Around 20 minutes.
    As short as 10 minutes; rarely as long as 60 minutes.
    Following delivery, mare lies quietly for 10 to 15 minutes with foal's hindlimbs still in the vagina.

Stage III - Expulsion of placental membranes
    Uterine contractions continue. Walk a distressed mare.
    Placental vessels collapse.
    Allantochorion is turned inside-out and rolled down the uterine horns as microcotyledons are freed from endometrial crypts.
    Time for Stage III: 1/2 hour to 3 hours after delivery.
    Placental membranes spread out on a flat surface should be complete and have a normal velvety appearance due to the microcotyledons on the inside-out allantochorion.

Plate 73

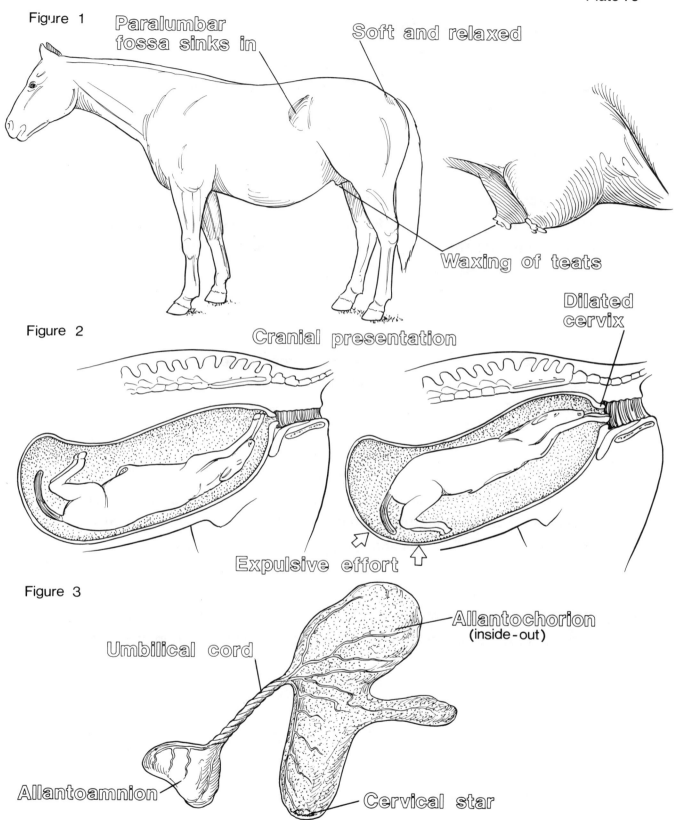

Figure 1

Paralumbar fossa sinks in

Soft and relaxed

Waxing of teats

Figure 2

Cranial presentation

Dilated cervix

Expulsive effort

Figure 3

Umbilical cord

Allantochorion (inside-out)

Allantoamnion

Cervical star

GENITAL ORGANS OF THE STALLION

Figure 1. Left lateral view of dissected male genital organs.
Figure 2. Diagrammatic drawing of the right testis and epididymis.

Spermatozoa (sperm cells) develop in **seminiferous tubules**, then pass through **straight tubules, rete tubules** and **efferent ducts** in the **head of the epididymis**. As spermatozoa pass through the **body of the epididymis**, they mature under the influence of secretions of the epithelium lining the epididymal duct. The **tail of the epididymis** and the first part of the **deferent duct** contain mature, motile spermatozoa with whip-like tails. The very muscular **deferent duct** continues from the tail of the epididymis up the **spermatic cord** through the inguinal canal, ending as the expanded **ampulla**. A cremaster muscle (detached from the internal abdominal oblique) covers the lateral aspect of each spermatic cord.

During ejaculation, each powerful deferent duct propels spermatozoa to the pelvic part of the **urethra** where they are joined by secretions from the ampullary glands, the **prostate gland** and the paired **seminal vesicles** and **bulbourethral glands**, forming semen.

Each **testis** (Latin), (English, testicle; Greek, orchid) is suspended by a fold of peritoneum, the mesorchium, and enclosed by its continuation, the **vaginal tunic**. Deep to the visceral part of the **vaginal tunic**, the dense fibrous connective tissue **tunica albuginea** and its internally projecting septa support the testis. The **scrotum** is a pouch of skin, smooth muscle, fascia and parietal vaginal tunic that contains the testicles. Smooth muscle in the scrotum and skeletal muscle of the external cremaster muscles assist in regulating the temperature of the testicles by raising and lowering them from the body wall. The left testicle is often larger than the right.

Plate 74

Figure 1

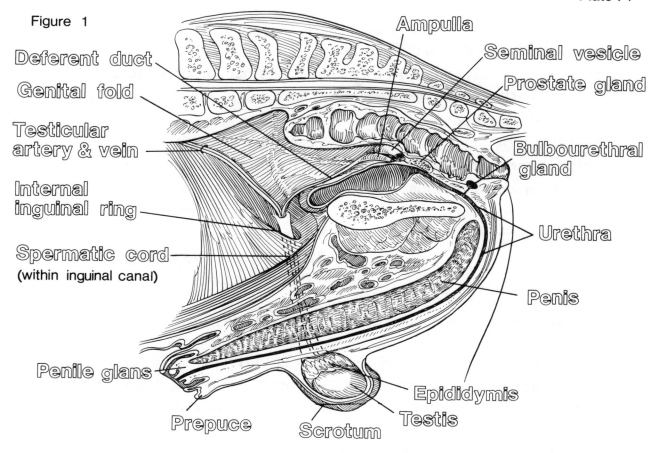

Deferent duct

Genital fold

Testicular artery & vein

Internal inguinal ring

Spermatic cord (within inguinal canal)

Penile glans

Prepuce

Scrotum

Testis

Epididymis

Penis

Urethra

Bulbourethral gland

Prostate gland

Seminal vesicle

Ampulla

Figure 2

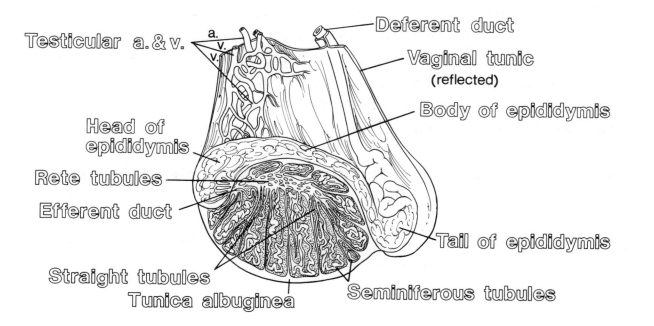

Testicular a. & v.

a.
v.
v.

Head of epididymis

Rete tubules

Efferent duct

Straight tubules

Tunica albuginea

Seminiferous tubules

Tail of epididymis

Body of epididymis

Vaginal tunic (reflected)

Deferent duct

Figure 1. Dorsal view of accessory sex glands.

Figure 2. Right lateral view of dissected penis.

Figure 3. End of penis protruding from prepuce. **External part of prepuce** cut. Dotted lines indicate the position of the **urethral sinus** dorsal to the **urethral process.**

1. **Urethral muscle**
2. **Ischiocavernous muscle**
3. **Retractor muscles of penis**
    (smooth muscle)
4. **Bulbospongiosus muscle**
5. **Genital fold**
6. **Bladder**

7. **Obturator artery**
8. **External pudendal artery**
9. **Cranial artery of penis**
10. **Middle artery of penis**
11. **Dorsal artery of penis**
12. **Suspensory lig. of penis**
13. **Urethral sinus**

Seminal vesicles add the greatest volume of secretion to semen. They do not store sperm cells.

The non-haired skin of the preputial lining as far as the preputial fold contains many sebaceous (oil) and sweat glands. A "bean" of cheesy smegma and dead cells may fill the **urethral sinus**. Excessive accumulations of smegma should be washed away.

The stallion has a musculocavernous penis. The **cavernous body** (L., corpus cavernosum) continues caudad on each side into a crus that attaches to the ischiadic arch. Vascular spaces enclosed by connective tissue and smooth muscle occur within the cavernous body and the spongy body (L., corpus spongiosum) surrounding the urethra. These spaces fill with blood during erection of the penis. The spongy body expands into the **glans penis**. Erection is brought about by relaxation of some small internal arteries, pumping action of the ischiocavernous muscles, and pressure against veins returning blood from the penis. The penis protrudes stiffly during erection.

"Flaring" is an enlargement of the glans penis during erection with the **crown** reaching a large diameter. It is noticeable just after the stallion dismounts from breeding.

During urination, the penis extends loosely from the prepuce. **Retractor muscles** act to pull the penis into the prepuce.

Plate 75

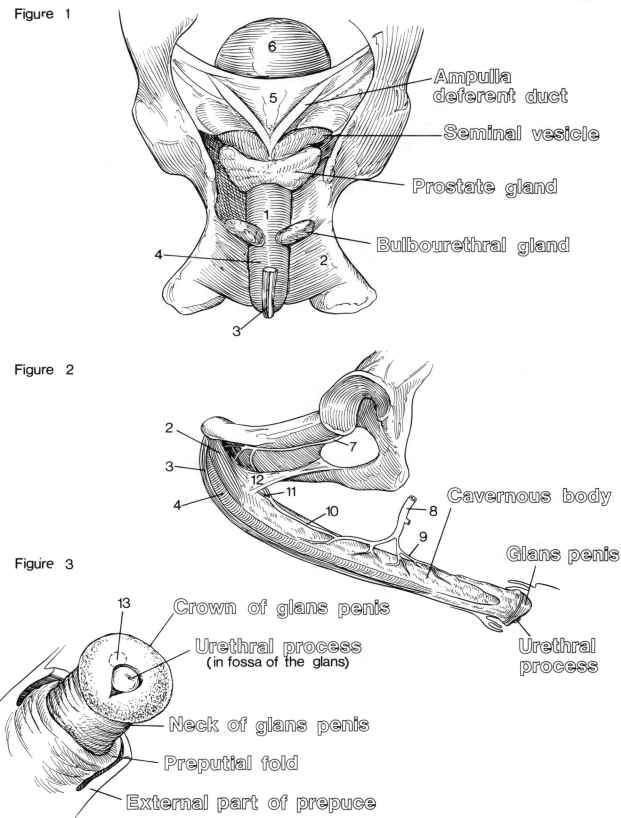

Figure 1

Ampulla
deferent duct

Seminal vesicle

Prostate gland

Bulbourethral gland

Figure 2

Cavernous body

Glans penis

Urethral
process

Figure 3

Crown of glans penis

Urethral process
(in fossa of the glans)

Neck of glans penis

Preputial fold

External part of prepuce

Figure 1. Caudal part of equine fetus on day 75 of gestation.

Figure 2. Caudal part of equine fetus on day 175 of gestation.

Figure 3. Caudal part of equine fetus near the time of birth.

The **testis** (plural = testes) begins as a swelling under the mesonephros (middle kidney). As the mesonephros is replaced by the final kidney (metanephros), the enlarging testis takes on the peritoneal covering of the mesonephros and becomes suspended by the **mesorchium.** The **mesonephric duct** does not regress but persists to become the **duct of the epididymis** and the **deferent duc**t.

The **gubernaculum** (L., helm) is a long mass of soft mucous connective tissue formed in a fold of peritoneum. The **gubernacular cord** part extends from the testis to the expanding **gubernacular bulb** that is associated with the outpocketing **vaginal process** of peritoneum.

The **inguinal canal** is a potential space between the internal abdominal oblique muscle and the fibrous aponeurosis of the external abdominal oblique muscle. A slit in the aponeurosis of the external abdominal oblique is the superficial inguinal ring. The gubernacular bulb grows and swells, dilating the vaginal ring (of the vaginal process) and the inguinal canal. This guides the descent of the testis. The testis is forced to descend by pressure from the peritoneal fluid and the intestinal mass. The loop formed by the tail of the epididymis and the deferent duct enters the inguinal canal first followed by the testis and the rest of the epididymis. Visceral peritoneum covers these structures and is continuous with the mesorchium. As the testis enters the **scrotum**, the soft gubernacular bulb changes to the short, fibrous proper ligament of the testis and the ligament of the tail of the epididymis.

Normally, both testes should descend into the scrotum between 30 days before and 10 days after birth.
There is a high incidence of cryptorchidism (Gr., hidden orchid) (or retained testicle) in the stallion. Among suggested reasons for this is the lack of normal reduction in size of the very large fetal testis to a smaller size before it descends into the inguinal canal. The testis may be retained within the abdominal cavity or within the inguinal canal. The term, high flanker, has been used to describe retention within the inguinal canal. A ridgling is a cryptorchid horse.

Plate 76

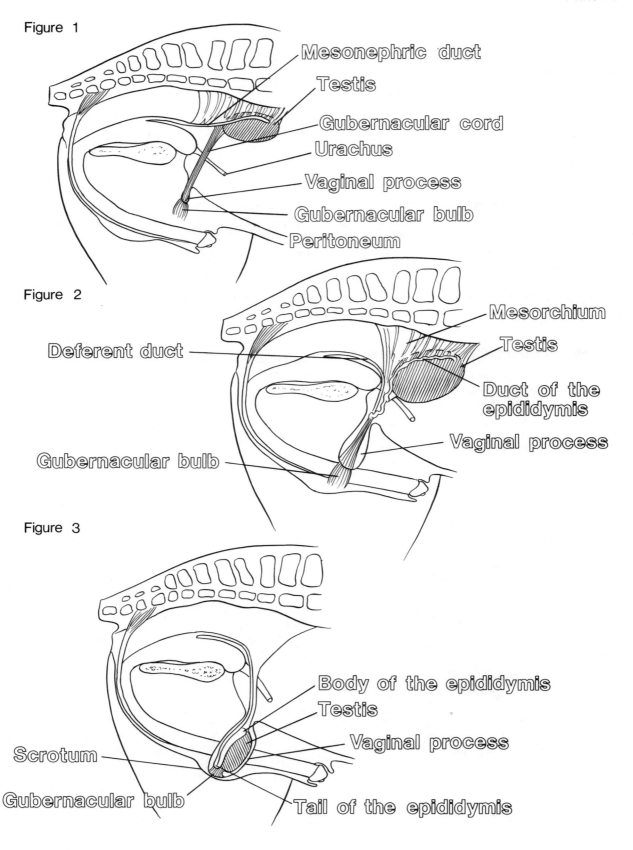

Figure 1

Mesonephric duct
Testis
Gubernacular cord
Urachus
Vaginal process
Gubernacular bulb
Peritoneum

Figure 2

Mesorchium
Testis
Deferent duct
Duct of the epididymis
Vaginal process
Gubernacular bulb

Figure 3

Body of the epididymis
Testis
Vaginal process
Scrotum
Gubernacular bulb
Tail of the epididymis

HORSE'S BRAIN

Figure 1. Dorsal view of brain.
Figure 2. Median section of brain.

1. **Longitudinal fissure**
2. **Right cerebral hemisphere**
3. **Sulci** (grooves)
4. **Gyri** (convolutions)
5. **Cerebellum**
6. **Corpus callosum**
        (connects cerebral hemispheres)
7. **Septum pellucidum**
8. **Pineal gland**

9. **Medulla oblongata**
10. **Pons**
11. **Thalamus**
12. **Hypothalamus**
13. **Pituitary gland**
14. **Infundibulum of 13**
15. **Optic chiasm**
16. **Olfactory bulb**
17. **Optic nerve**

The **pineal gland** and **pituitary gland** are <u>endocrine</u> <u>organs</u> attached to the brain.

Plate 77

Figure 1

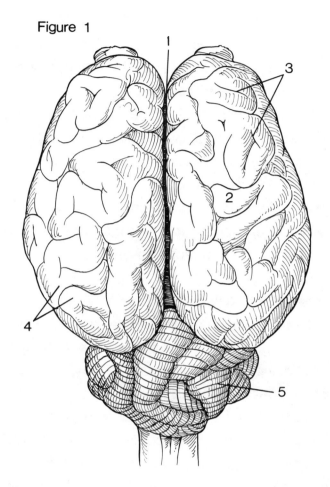

Figure 2

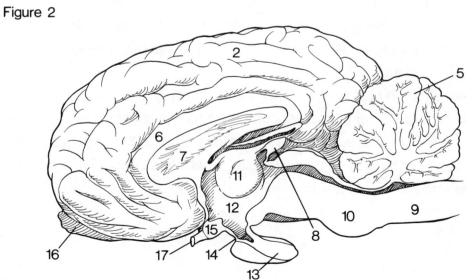

Ventral view of brain and cranial nerve roots.

I. Olfactory nerve - Sense of smell. Many small nerve fibers come from the mucous membrane of the nasal cavity through openings in the cribriform plate of the ethmoid bone to the **olfactory bulb.**

II. Optic nerve - Vision. Some of the fibers coming from the retina of one eye cross over at the **optic chiasm** and continue into the optic tract on the opposite side.

III. Oculomotor nerve - Motor to several extraocular muscles. Parasympathetic fibers to intrinsic eye muscles.

IV. Trochlear nerve - Motor to a single extraocular muscle.

V. Trigeminal nerve - Sensory to face. Motor to muscles of mastication and deep muscles of head. Sensory to teeth. Lingual branch sensory for touch to the tongue.

VI. Abducent nerve - Motor to two extraocular muscles.

VII. Facial nerve - Motor to facial, eyelid and ear muscles. Its chorda tympani branch joins the lingual nerve to mediate taste to the rostral 2/3 of the tongue. Parasympathetic supply to lacrimal and salivary glands.

VIII. Vestibulocochlear nerve - Sensory for hearing and balance.

IX. Glossopharyngeal nerve - Motor to muscles of palate and pharynx. Mediates taste from caudal 1/3 of tongue. Sensory to mucous membrane of palate and pharynx. Parasympathetic supply to salivary glands.

X. Vagus nerve - Parasympathetic nerves to smooth muscle of cervical, thoracic and abdominal viscera. Sensory to external ear. Sensory to laryngeal mucous membrane and motor to intrinsic laryngeal muscles via cranial and caudal laryngeal nerves.

XI. Accessory nerve (spinal root) - The spinal root is formed by tiny rootlets from the cervical region of the spinal cord. It forms the accessory nerve motor to four shoulder muscles. A <u>cranial</u> <u>root</u> from caudal to the vagal roots sends fibers to the vagus nerve that eventually reach the caudal laryngeal nerve.

XII. Hypoglossal nerve - Motor to muscles of the tongue.

Plate 78

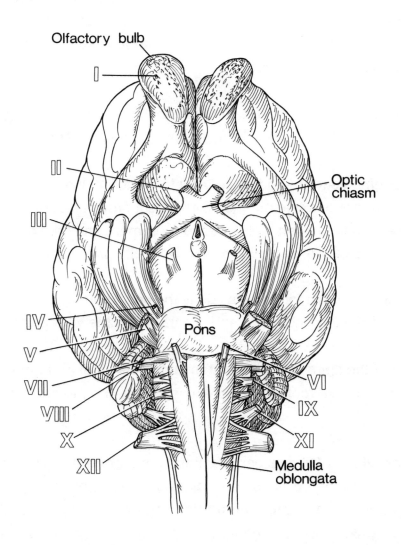

Olfactory bulb

I

II

III

IV

V

VII

VIII

X

XII

Optic chiasm

Pons

VI

IX

XI

Medulla oblongata

Figure 1. Schematic dorsal view of spinal cord.
Figure 2. Cross section of thoracic spinal cord and its relationships to the vertebral
          canal and spinal nerves.

1. **Epidural space** (of vertebral canal)
2. **Meninges** (singular, meninx)
3. **Spinal cord**
4 **Dorsal root**
5. **Dorsal root ganglion**
     (collection of nerve cell bodies)

6. **Ventral root**
7. **Thoracic spinal nerve**
8. **Communicating branches to
     sympathetic trunk**
9. **Sympathetic trunk**

The spinal cord continues from the medulla oblongata at the foramen magnum,
extending caudad to the caudal half of the second sacral vertebra.

Spinal cord segments from the first cervical to the fourth lumbar are in the vertebral
canal of the vertebra of same number. Differential growth and displacement ac-
counts for the presence of an eighth cervical segment and the final positions of
lumbar, sacral and caudal segments cranial to their corresponding vertebra.

The **cauda equina** (Latin for horse's tail) is the collection of spinal nerve roots that
extend caudad from the end of the spinal cord within the vertebral canal.

The diameter of the spinal cord is greatest at the **cervical** and **lumbar enlarge-
ments** where the nerve roots for the plexuses supplying the nerves of the limbs
originate.

A sensory **dorsal root** (with its ganglion) and a motor **ventral root** join to form a
spinal nerve, which then divides into major dorsal and ventral branches. In the
thoracic and **lumbar regions, communicating branches** go to and come from the
sympathetic trunk, a series of ganglia connected by nerve lying along the inner
surface of the thoracic wall.

The dura mater, outermost meninx covering the spinal cord, is separated from the
wall of the vertebral canal by an epidural space containing adipose tissue and an
internal vertebral venous plexus.

Plate 79

Figure 1

Cervical region

Cervical
enlargement

Thoracic region

Lumbar region

Lumbar enlargement

Sacral and caudal regions

Cauda equina

Figure 2

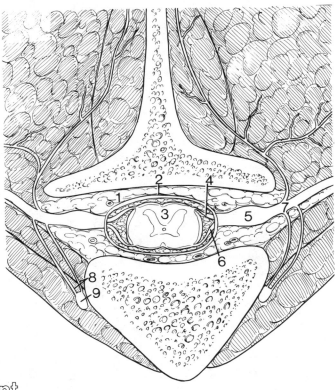

Plate 80

AUTONOMIC NERVOUS SYSTEM

Parasympathetic division: stippled; sympathetic division: black.

1. Parasympathetic nuclei (collection of nerve cell bodies) in the brainstem. Source of parasympathetic fibers for nerves III, VII, IX and X **(vagus nerve).**

2. Cranial cervical ganglion (collection of nerve cell bodies). Source of sympathetic nerve fibers supplying the head.

3. Vertebral nerve

4. Sympathetic trunk and ganglia

5. Large sympathetic ganglia

6. Sympathetic nerves to thoracic, abdominal and pelvic organs

7. Vagal nerve branches to thoracic and abdominal organs

8. Pelvic nerves - parasympathetic supply to pelvic organs

The **vagus nerve** and **sympathetic trunk** are sheathed together as the vagosympathetic trunk that lies adjacent to the common carotid artery in the neck.

Both divisions of the autonomic nervous system are described as motor, but sensory nerve fibers course in autonomic nerves.

Nerve fibers from nerve cell bodies in the lateral gray horns of the thoracolumbar spinal cord synapse with (pass nerve impulses to) nerve cells in sympathetic ganglia. Nerve fibers from cell bodies in the ganglia supply sympathetic innervation to the organs. Parasympathetic ganglia are within or on the organs that they supply with nerve fibers.

Parasympathetic and sympathetic nerves usually supply the same organs, causing different responses:

ORGAN	PARASYMPATHETIC EFFECTS	SYMPATHETIC EFFECTS
Eye	Constriction of pupil	Dilation of pupil
Lacrimal glands	Secretion	Decreased secretion
Salivary glands	Secretion	Decreased secretion: contraction of myoepithelial cells
Heart	Decreased contraction rate	Increased contraction rate
Bronchi	Constriction	Relaxation
Stomach & intestines	Increased motility & secretion	Decreased activity
Adrenal medulla	No effect	Secretion of epinephrine
Bladder	Contraction	Relaxation

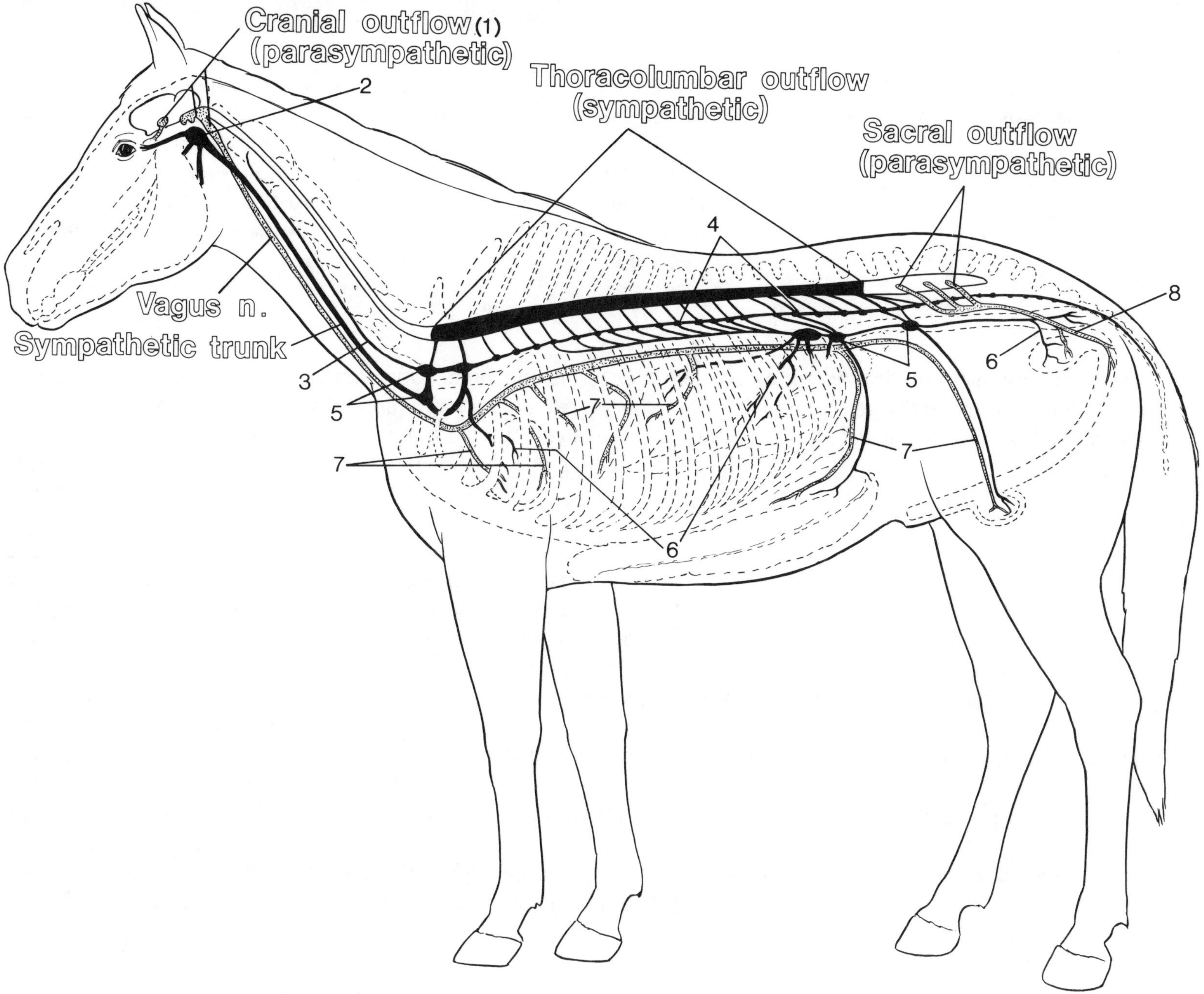

Cranial outflow (1)
(parasympathetic)

Thoracolumbar outflow
(sympathetic)

Sacral outflow
(parasympathetic)

Vagus n.

Sympathetic trunk

2

3

4

5

6

7

8

Plate 80

Plate 81

MENINGES AND CEREBROSPINAL FLUID

Schematic drawing showing:

*The meninges (singular, meninx) - three membranes covering the brain and spinal cord.

* Main sites of production of cerebrospinal fluid (CSF) - **choroid plexuses.** CSF is also produced by the lining of the ventricles and brain tissue.

*Circulation of CSF (arrows) through the **ventricles** (communicating chambers in the brain), the **central canal** of the spinal cord, and the **subarachnoid space.**

*Drainage of CSF through projecting **arachnoid granulations** into blood of **venous sinuses** within the **dura mater.**

*End of spinal cord and **cauda equina.**

*Sites for withdrawal of CSF and for injection of anesthetic into epidural space (epidural anesthesia).

1. **Dura mater of cranial cavity** (blends with the periosteum of the cranial vault)
2. **Dura mater of vertebral canal** - dense fibrous outer meninx
3. **Epidural space** (only in vertebral canal) - contains fat, vessels and nerves
4. **Periosteum of vertebral canal**
5. **Arachnoid membrane**
6. **Subarachnoid space** (greatly enlarged here) - contains CSF
   Crossed by spider-web-like filaments from the arachnoid membrane to the pia mater
7. **Pia mater** - vascular membrane covering the brain and spinal cord; forms **terminal filament** at end of spinal cord
8. **Cerebellomedullary cistern** - enlargement of subarachnoid space; clinical site for obtaining a sample of CSF
9. **Interventricular foramen** - one on each side; connects lateral ventricle in cerebral hemisphere with third ventricle
10. **Third ventricle** - in midbrain
11. **Choroid plexus of third ventricle**
12. **Fourth ventricle** - in medulla oblongata
13. **Central canal of spinal cord** - continues caudad from fourth ventricle
14. **Choroid plexus of fourth ventricle**
15. **Lateral aperture of fourth ventricle** - carries CSF to subarachnoid space
16. **Arachnoid granulations** - projecting into the dorsal sagittal venous sinus
17. **Dorsal sagittal venous sinus**

CSF functions: cushion the brain and spinal cord; transport nutrients, waste products and regulatory substances.
Hydrocephalus is an excessive accumulation of CSF.

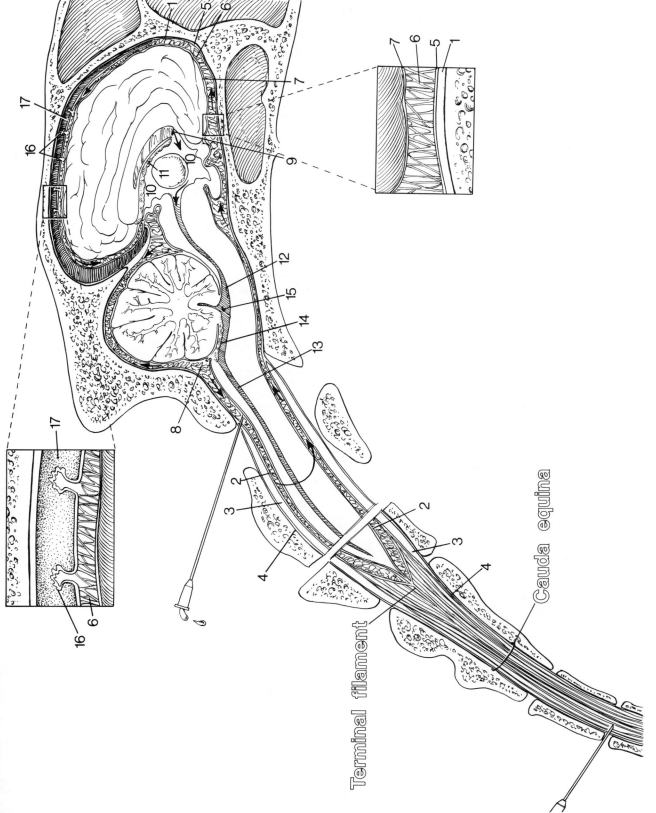

Terminal filament

Cauda equina

Plate 81

NOTES

NOTES

NOTES

NOTES

NOTES

NOTES

NOTES

INDEX

The plate numbers following the words refer to the narrative on the left page as well as the drawing(s) on the right page. All terms are listed under a main term. For example, to find Coffin bone, look under Bone(s), coffin.